Mud & Stars

The Report of a Working Party on
The Impact of Hospice Experience
on the Church's Ministry of Healing

SOBELL PUBLICATIONS

Sobell Publications
Sir Michael Sobell House
Churchill Hospital
Oxford OX3 7LJ

ISBN-0-9517537-2-X

Printed in Great Britain by Billings & Sons Limited, Worcester

Contents

*"Two men looked through prison bars;
one saw mud and the other stars."*

Preface

In recent years many local churches and communities have come to see healing as part of their ministry - hence 'the ministry of healing'. Simultaneously, there has been increased concern for the needs of the dying - hence the modern hospice. The insights and strengths of both movements, however, have not generally been integrated. This is a matter for regret because, almost certainly, both have much to learn from and to give to each other. Instead, separate development has led to misunderstandings and antagonism.

In an attempt to bridge the gap, an inter-denominational Working Party comprising mainly doctors, nurses and clergy was set up to examine **the Impact of Hospice Experience on the Church's Ministry of Healing**. Fourteen plenary sessions were held at Sir Michael Sobell House, Oxford, between January 1989 and May 1991. In addition, there were two residential meetings at the Abbey, Sutton Courtenay.

In pursuing its task, the Working Party envisaged that the readers of the Report would include theological students, other pastoral care students, hospital chaplains, parochial clergy, church study groups, medical students, doctors, nurses, other health-care workers, and hospice staff.

The Working Party wishes to acknowledge financial support received from:

The Archbishop of Canterbury (Lord Runcie)
12 Anglican bishops
Joseph Rank Benevolent Trust
Help the Hospices
Culham Educational Foundation
Margaret Houghton Memorial Fund
Discovery Foundation
Guild of St Barnabas

Without their backing, the Working Party could not have come into being and pursued its task.

The Working Party is grateful to Professor John Rogerson and Rev Ian Woodroffe for each attending a meeting, and to Canon Norman Autton and Rev Helen Walker for written submissions. The Working Party also wishes to record its gratitude to Miss Karen Jones and Mrs Susan Boreham for their long-suffering and diligent help in preparing the Report for publication.

Robert Twycross

Members of the Working Party

Dr Robert Twycross

Clinical Reader in Palliative Medicine, University of Oxford (Chairman)

Canon John Barton

former Chaplain, John Radcliffe Hospital, Oxford

Mrs Prue Clench

Consultant in Palliative Care Management and Education, St Austell

Ms Virginia Dunn

Senior Lecturer in Palliative Care, South Bank Polytechnic, London

Dr David Frampton

Medical Director, Chelmsford Hospice Service, Chelmsford

Rev Brian Greet

former Methodist District Chairman and Hospice Chaplain, Derby

Mr Peter Harvey

Free-lance writer and speaker on theological topics, Birmingham

Canon Tom Curtis-Hayward

Catholic priest, Stroud

Rev Colin Kassell

Hospice Chaplain & Pastoral Leader, St Catherine's Hospice, Crawley

Dr Jean Kay

Community Hospice Team, Brighton

Rev Leonard Lunn

Hospice Chaplain, St Christopher's Hospice, London

Ms Marilyn Marks

Director of Nursing, Trinity Hospice, London

Venerable Michael Paton

former Anglican Archdeacon of Sheffield Diocese, Sheffield

Miss Patricia Scott	Senior Nurse, Sir Michael Sobell House, Oxford
Rev Ian Ainsworth-Smith	Hospital Chaplain, St George's Hospital, London
Dr Gareth Tuckwell	Medical Director, Dorothy Kerin Trust, Burrswood, Groombridge
Rev Dr Michael Wilson	retired priest and doctor, Birmingham

Dr Derek Munday	General Practitioner & General Secretary, Caring Professions Concern, Reading (withdrew 1990 because of other commitments)
Rev Dr John Young	Director, Churches' Council for Health and Healing, St Marylebone Church, London (died February 1991)

Acknowledgements

All quotations from the Bible are taken from the **Revised English Bible** unless stated otherwise.

The Working Party is grateful to the copyright holders for permission to include the following:

Afraid by F Julian (p 13). In: Eishenhauer J (ed). *Traveller's Tales: Poetry from Hospice*. Marshall Pickering, London 1989.
Figure 1 by Averil Stedeford (p 89). In: Stedeford A. *Facing Death: Patients, Families and Professionals*. Heinemann, London 1984.
Why Me? by S Crosher (p 94). In: *Good Grief*. Cruse, London 1987.

Case History by Eric Cassell (pp 130-31). In: *New England Journal of Medicine* 1982.
Death in the First Person (p 145). In: *American Journal of Nursing* 1970.
When I shall die by Anna (p 146). In: Fynn. *Mister God, This is Anna*. Collins, London 1974.
Drawings by Sheila Cassidy (pp 147-8). In: Cassidy S. *Sharing the Darkness*. Darton, Longman & Todd, London 1988.
Forgiveness by Brenda Dawson (p 157). In: Saunders C (ed). *St Christopher's in Celebration: 21 years at Britain's first modern hospice*. Hodder & Stoughton, London 1988.
An extract by William Coffin (pp 159-60). In: *Thanatos* 1989.

An extract by Bishop John V Taylor (p 162). In: Taylor JV. *Weep not for me*. World Council of Churches, Geneva 1985.
An extract by M Williams (p 169). In: Williams M. *The Velveteen Rabbit*. Heinemann, London 1922.
Table 1 by Mary Vachon (p 182). In: *Quality Review Bulletin* 1979.

Before the Anaesthetic by John Betjeman (p 209). In: *Collected Poems*. John Murray, London 1958.

SECTION I : HOSPICE

---

1 HOSPICE CARE

Hospice is a programme of care for terminally ill patients and their families. In practice, most patients have cancer. The word hospice, 'a resting place for travellers or pilgrims', was popularized by Dame Cicely Saunders, who founded St Christopher's Hospice, London in 1967. It was felt to reflect a type of care which incorporated the skills of a hospital and the more leisurely hospitality and warmth of a home.[1] In the hospice, the centre of interest shifts from the disease to the patient and family, from the pathological process to the person. The main goals of hospice care are to provide:[2,3]

- relief for patients from pain and other distressing symptoms
- psychological and spiritual care for patients so that they may come to terms with and prepare for their own death as fully as they can
- a support system to help the patients live as actively and creatively as possible until death, thereby promoting autonomy, personal integrity and self-esteem
- a support system to help families cope during the patient's illness and in bereavement.

Patients with terminal disease often need more care than those whose sickness is curable. The hospice offers 'intensive terminal care'. Professional skills of a high order are required: "expert care that is individual to the patient, detailed, sensitive, and time consuming".[4]

Although hospice philosophy is not limited by 'the tyranny of cure', it is steadfastly opposed to euthanasia. Hospice both affirms life and recognizes dying as a normal process. It therefore seeks neither to hasten nor to postpone death.[5]

Hospice care is distinct from geriatric medicine and the care of the chronically sick, two specialities with which it is frequently compared. According to one doctor, hospice care:

> "Contains many of the rewards of surgery, since it operates in a setting of crisis intervention; of internal medicine, since it calls for the fine titration of drug regimens against troublesome symptoms; and of psychiatry, since it deals with the anxious, the depressed and the bereaved."[6]

Hospice care implies a comprehensive approach which considers not only physical but also psychological, social and spiritual issues.

Christian Tradition and Hospice Management

The parable of the compassionate Samaritan (Luke 10.30-35) and the well-known quotation, "Anything you did for one of my brothers here, you did for me" (Matt.25.40) have inspired Christians in every generation to minister to the destitute and dying. Thus, although the care of the dying is not an exclusively Christian activity, many hospices have been founded by those who felt led by God to undertake the task, and have sought to incorporate the principles and traditions of their faith. St Christopher's Hospice, London, is one such example:

> "St Christopher's Hospice is a religious foundation, based on the full Christian faith in God, through Christ. Its aim is to express the love of God to all who come,

in every possible way; in skilled nursing and medical
care, in the use of every scientific means of relieving
suffering and distress, in understanding, personal
sympathy, with respect for the dignity of each patient
as a human being, precious to God and man."[7]

This has considerable implications for the hospice staff,
volunteers and supporters, and sometimes has led to confusion
and misunderstanding. As subsequent generations of staff
have been appointed, it has been necessary to identify these
often unwritten expectations and question their authority.

A Concept of Care

Although St Christopher's was not the first modern hospice,
its impact led to the 'hospice movement'. There are now few
communities in Britain that do not have some access to a
form of hospice care. Because it has not always been
possible or desirable to build a separate institution, a variety
of approaches has been adopted, including home-care
hospice programmes and hospital symptom-control teams.
These alternative approaches emphasize that 'hospice' is a
concept of care which is not dependent on a building for
implementation.

Hospice seeks to prevent **last** days becoming **lost** days. It
attempts to do this by offering a type of care which is
appropriate to the needs of the dying. Although it has been
described as 'low tech and high touch', hospice is not against
modern medical technology. Rather it seeks to ensure that
love and not science is the controlling force in patient care.
'High tech' investigations and treatments are used only when
their benefits clearly outweigh any potential burdens. Thus,
science is used in the service of love, and not *vice versa*. In
summary, hospice care is an attempt to re-establish the
traditional role of doctors and other clinical staff:

> "to cure sometimes,
> to relieve often,
> to comfort always."

Hope

It is easier to have hope when all is going well. Disappointments and failure, however, make hope more difficult, and sometimes a sense of hopelessness ensues. In helping patients overcome this, it is important that the nature of hope is understood. Often it is confused with magical thinking; as if by wishing for something we could bring it into being:

> "To wish for something to be different is a passive emotion and tends to lead toward wanting someone to effect a magical solution. Hope, on the other hand, is a goal-directed vision that enables one to live effectively in the present and move trustingly toward future possibilities."[8]

There is a difference between giving up hope and giving up a particular hope. It is cruel to deprive a person of hope. The crucial question is: for what is the person hoping? A frequent task of hospice staff (and of others who care for the dying) is to help a person transfer hope from one object to another; from a hope that is becoming unrealistic to one that has more promise for sustaining the person through the crisis of approaching death. It may become, quite simply, the promise that the person will not be left to face death alone.

Hope diminishes when:[9]
- the patient is mentally isolated by a 'conspiracy of silence'
- it is implied that there is nothing more which can be done
- pain and other symptoms remain unrelieved

4

- symptoms such as depression are ignored
- the patient feels alone or unsupported
- spiritual distress is not recognized
- the future seems to be no more than an insuperable mountain of problems and/or unrelieved catastrophe.

Hospice care aims to restore hope by offering patients **unconditional acceptance** and **affirmation of self-worth**. In practice, these are conveyed by attitude and action, for example by:

- taking time to explain what is happening
- giving the patient a direction in which to move by setting priorities and establishing realistic goals
- improving the relief of pain and other troublesome symptoms
- establishing trust between the clinical staff and the patient and family.

Working towards realistic goals breaks the vicious circle of despair, and ends the nightmare prospect of never-ending pain or other physical discomfort.

Skilled Companionship

The fear has been expressed that palliative care could become just one more 'technique' within contemporary high-technology mainstream medicine - a technique behind which professionals could hide and through which they could soullessly exercise 'power'.[10] This remains a continuing danger. It probably can be avoided, however, if the basis of hospice care remains companionship - the companionship of professional staff with those who are dying.

In a crisis we need a companion. When dying we need a companion who can explain in straightforward terms why there is pain, or shortness of breath, or constipation, or weakness. Explanation is a key component of treatment because, psychologically, it cuts the illness and the symptoms down to size because they are no longer shrouded in total mystery. This is reassuring.

Skilled companionship has been described as 'friendly professional interest' (FPI):[11]

> "FPI suits any age, any race, any culture, any faith (or none), any philosophy of care, and any prognosis. It is also exactly the same for patients who 'know' as for those who don't."

Unfortunately, not all doctors are able to offer FPI:

> "One of the doctors in the practice calls in nearly every day but it seems to be just to check that I'm still alive, they don't actually do anything. I've told them to stop coming so often".

If these doctors had called less often, but with real FPI, they would have given more help and taken less time.

> "A widow spoke of how the doctor came and said, 'there's no point in visiting your husband, there's nothing we can do for him'."

Then she changed to another doctor:

> "And he was marvellous... he put my husband's mind at rest... if you've got some moral support you can carry on. He visited him once a week."

How one person is able to give strength to another is a mystery. Brewin suggests that just being natural and friendly has much to do with it, and cites the way in which many hospital cleaners and porters are able to cheer up patients:

"Do they have special understanding, spiritual inspiration, or powers of leadership? Not usually. How many communication and counselling courses have they attended? None. They are just natural and relaxed, with friendly good humour and no awkwardness or embarrassment."[11]

In other words, they offer **unconditional acceptance** and **affirmation of self-worth**. For clinical staff, this means communicating the following message:

"Whatever happens we will not abandon you" (acceptance)
"You are important to us" (affirmation).

This twin message has to be lived rather than spoken, and it is in the living of it that clinical staff become truly supportive.

Towards Fully Personal Care

Relief of pain and other distressing symptoms is rightly seen as the primary goal of hospice care. Expertise in symptom control has reached a point where patients can expect to be almost free of pain.[12] A high measure of relief can also be expected with most other symptoms. No longer distracted and exhausted by unrelieved pain, patients may become distressed emotionally and spiritually as they contemplate their approaching death. Few do this with equilibrium; most defend themselves psychologically in a variety of ways; and some are overwhelmed with anguish, rage, or fear about what is happening to them.

In consequence, it has been suggested that a hospice should be thought of as "a safe place to suffer":[3]

"They need to know that their turmoil and distress is a sign that they are making a major adjustment, and not that they are going mad, for the fear of madness is even greater than the fear of death."[3]

It is necessary to offer fully personal care (Table 1). The staff aim to help the patient do his best, given his personality, his family, his cultural background, his beliefs, his age, his illness, his symptoms, his anxieties, and his fears. The patient and family comprise the unit of care. There is need for flexibility; patients must be met where they are socially, culturally, psychologically and spiritually as well as physically. There is no such being as a typical dying patient.

'Spiritual' embraces the essence of what it means to be human. It is concerned with 'right-relatedness' and includes those experiences in human life which transcend sensory phenomena. Such experiences tend to give rise to theological reflections, religious responses and ethical beliefs. The spiritual aspect may also be viewed as the integrating component, holding together the physical, psychological and social components. It is often perceived as being concerned with meaning and purpose. For those nearing the end of life, it is commonly associated with a need for forgiveness, reconciliation and affirmation of worth.

There is much written about the emotional needs of the dying;[13,14] far less about spiritual aspects of care. Human life, however, is not governed simply by instincts and hormones.[15] Human desire extends beyond the basic human needs of food, comfort, and companionship. People are questioning and questing creatures who ask, 'Why?' As Nietzsche said: "He who has a why to live can bear almost any how."

Table 1   Needs of the dying

Dimension	Need
Physical	Relief of symptoms
Psychological	
Safety	Feeling of security
Understanding	Explanation about symptoms and the disease; opportunity to discuss the process of dying
Self-esteem	Involvement in decision-making, particularly as physical dependency on others increases; opportunity to give as well as to receive
Social	
Acceptance	Non-condemnatory attitude in the carers regardless of one's mood, sociability, and appearance
Belonging	Feeling needed and connected; *not* a burden
Disengagement	Opportunity to take leave of those people or things to whom one is attached; to 'tie up loose ends' in business and family matters; to hand on responsibility to others
Spiritual	
Love	Expressions of affection; human contact, e.g. touch
Reconciliation	Opportunity for healing damaged relationships; and to seek forgiveness
Self-worth	Knowledge that one is loved and valued
Purpose	Feeling one's life still has meaning and direction

When newly-released from concentration camp, Viktor Frankl wrote:

> "Another time we were at work in a trench. The dawn was gray around us... I was struggling to find the reason for my sufferings, my slow dying. In a last violent protest against the hopelessness of imminent death, I sensed my spirit piercing through the enveloping gloom. I felt it transcend that hopeless, meaningless world and from somewhere I heard a victorious 'Yes' in answer to my question of the existence of an ultimate purpose. At that moment a light was lit in a distant farmhouse...in the midst of the miserable gray of a dawning morning in Bavaria." [16]

The modern hospice is historically rooted in Christian belief, although in practice it is more broadly theistic. A Jewish involvement has been evident from the early days and there is now a Buddhist Hospice Association. To work with the dying demands a belief in life, whether expressed or not. Life is seen as having meaning and purpose throughout the terminal illness.

This conviction is manifested primarily by attitudes and deeds rather than by words; more in how we respond to the dying and care for them than by what we say. As always, actions speak louder than words. The unspoken message has been succinctly summarized by Cicely Saunders:

> "You matter because you are you.
> You matter to the last moment of your life,
> and we will do all we can
> not only to help you die peacefully,
> but to live until you die."

It is this unspoken message that brings a sense of security to those cared for. Many patients say, "It is wonderful to feel safe." This security enables individual patients to consider within themselves fundamental questions concerning life, God, and the hereafter. Such contemplation is facilitated by the physical comfort which hospices provide. Spiritual care, therefore, may well be non-verbal, but nonetheless real for that.

When dying, many people take stock of their lives for the first time:

> 'Why should it happen to me?'
> 'What have I done to deserve this?'
> 'Did I do something wrong?'
> 'Did I get my priorities right?'
> 'I could have done more for other people.'
> 'I wish I'd given more time to my family.'

Only a minority of patients discuss these matters with their doctor, although the majority do so with a nurse, a social worker, or with relatives and close friends. People are perceptive, and patients are unlikely to embarrass a doctor (or indeed a clergyman) if they sense that communication at this level will cause discomfort.

The doctor's primary responsibility, however, is to help maintain an environment which is enabling for the patient. This requires relief from pain and other distressing symptoms. One result of this is that the patient is better able to consider more fundamental issues.

Restoring Creativity

> "Carers tend to have a preoccupation with treatment of one sort or another, things **done to** the patient or **for** the patient for his benefit. Terminally ill patients already have to have so much done for them that often they have lost all sense of purpose and worth." [17]

A hospice will try whenever possible to promote self-esteem by helping patients to be creative in appropriate ways. This is an important component of spiritual care. It leads people to develop their own potential and express their own personality further. It frees them to look more positively at deeper questions about meaning and purpose in living and dying, questions which become more insistent with the approach of death. Emphasis on the patient 'doing' rather than 'being done to' helps her to live and die more as a whole person.

It is important, however, not to push patients into unwanted activity. Skills and opportunities may have been lost, physical disability may make former hobbies inappropriate, or there may never have been sufficient space for recreation in their lives. But in many cases, gentle and imaginative encouragement entices an apathetic patient to do something that engenders an increased sense of well-being.

An added difficulty is that lethargy may make it difficult to get a patient to leave the bedside, and there are some who are totally bedfast. It is necessary, therefore, to bring activity to the patient in an attractive and not too demanding way rather than wait for him to make the move. Some hospices encourage creativity through writing, poetry and art.[17] Experienced artists are used who can prepare materials and support the patient in such a way that, despite limited strength and concentration, something of value is produced:

- a gift for a loved one
- a reminiscence to share with others
- a poem to challenge the carers.

Afraid

I am afraid of death;
death rather than dying;
fear of the unknown.

Nothing is worse than death.

Life is terribly important.
ANY sort of life -
just being alive...

Life is important even if
the importance of life
is sometimes hidden...

Life is important because
I am afraid of death.[18]

Teamwork

When considered as a whole, it is apparent that hospice care cannot be administered by any one individual, only by a group of people working together as a team. The composition of the team may vary but includes first the patient and then the immediate family, friends, doctor(s), nurses, social worker, therapists, priest and, on occasion, lawyer. Roles may become blurred (see chapter 9). But the team is corporately concerned for the well-being of the patient and the family - physical, psychological, social and spiritual.

References

1   Saunders CM. *The Management of Terminal Disease (2nd edn)*. Edward Arnold, London 1984.
2   Twycross RG. Hospice Care. In: Spilling R (ed). *Terminal Care at Home*. Oxford University Press, Oxford 1986, pp 96-112.
3   Stedeford A. Hospice: a safe place to suffer? *Palliative Medicine* 1987; **1**: 73-74.
4   Luxton RW. The modern hospice and its challenge to medicine. *British Medical Journal* 1979; **ii**: 583-584
5   National Hospice Organization (USA). *Standards of a Hospice Program of Care*, 1981.
6   Mount BM. Hospice care. *Journal of the Royal Society of Medicine* 1980; **73**: 471-473.
7   Wald F. *In Quest of the Spiritual Component of Care for the Terminally Ill*. Yale University, New Haven 1986.
8   Dobihal EF, Stewart CW. *When a Friend is Dying*. Abingdon Press, Nashville 1984.
9   Herth K. Fostering hope in terminally-ill people. *Journal of Advanced Nursing* 1990; **15**: 1250-1259.
10 O'Donovan O. *Some Theological Questions About Death and Dying*. Paper given to Oxford Field Group of Institute of Religion and Medicine, February 1982.
11 Brewin TB. Not TLC but FPI. *Journal of the Royal Society of Medicine* 1990; **83**: 172-175.
12 Expert Committee Report. *Cancer Pain Relief and Palliative Care*. Technical Report Series, No 804. WHO, Geneva 1990.

13 Kubler-Ross E. *On Death and Dying.* Tavistock, London 1970.

14 Stedeford A. *Facing Death: Patients, Families and Professionals.* Heinemann, London 1984.

15 Hardy AC. *The Spiritual Nature of Man.* Clarendon Press, Oxford 1979.

16 Frankl V. *Man's Search for Meaning.* Pocket Books, New York 1963.

17 Frampton DR. Restoring creativity to the dying patient. *British Medical Journal* 1986; **293**: 1593-1595.

18 Julian F. Afraid. In: Eisenhauer J (ed). *Traveller's Tales: Poetry from Hospice.* Marshall Pickering, London 1989.

2 THEOLOGY OF SUFFERING

In the face of death, our own questions and those of others about the meaning of life and suffering are sharpened. Who is God for the Job of today? Who is God for those who befriend Job, not just for a day, but day after day in shared anguish unto death?

It would be misguided to suppose that there is a cluster of insights comprehensive enough to encompass everything that is meant by 'suffering'. The Latin verb 'to suffer' has a common origin with 'patient' and 'passion' and is not necessarily restricted in meaning to physical pain. The hard questions here would be **why** we find ourselves in situations where supposedly free and responsible beings are entirely in the hands of others, and **how** we are to bear our helplessness. The loss of our cherished independence, even if an illusion, can pose this question very sharply. In what follows the word 'suffering' will be used mainly in the common modern English sense to connote severe physical pain or mental distress.

It is obviously humane to seek to prevent or minimize suffering. Equally it is appropriate to look for a meaning in suffering in terms of the divine purpose. Both these emphases are exemplified in a variety of ways in the history of the Church, but if pressed to extremes they become not only mutually contradictory but life-denying. To insist on stopping suffering at almost any cost may distract from the search for meaning. Yet to insist on a meaning, particularly if what is offered is a moralistic explanation, may complicate the task of easing the suffering, while deepening the unhappiness or guilt of those sufferers who see no such meaning. Even the noble words of Frankl carry a potential for oppression in their absoluteness:

"If there is a meaning in life at all, then there must be a meaning in suffering. Suffering is an ineradicable part of life, even as fate and death. Without suffering and human death, life cannot be complete." [1]

It has been said that the Christian answer to the mystery of suffering is not an explanation but a Presence. This is appealing but fails to encompass those situations where the cutting edge of the suffering is a felt Absence:

"My God, my God, why have you forsaken me?" (Matt.27.46)

"Where is God?... Go to him when your need is desperate, when all other help is vain, and what do you find? A door slammed in your face, and a sound of bolting... on the inside. After that, silence... What can this mean? Why is he so present a commander in our time of prosperity and so very absent a help in time of trouble?" [2]

It is wiser to say that suffering is incomprehensible and points to a greater mystery. Any attempt to make suffering comprehensible by some explanation or theory is always in danger of denying the mystery. Such theorizing reduces the uniqueness and mystery of a human life. Suffering people are offered a pre-packaged solution into which they must fit. The point is that the mystery of suffering points to the mystery of everything.

To picture a world without suffering as an alternative to our world is a fantasy. Suffering is so organically and inescapably part of our world that a world without it is not imaginable. This is the only world we know, the only world we have, the only world available to our scrutiny. We cannot stand outside this world and judge it to be deficient in so far as it features suffering. The question 'Why doesn't a loving God allow a world without suffering?' leads nowhere.

What needs to be asked instead is 'What is God doing?' or, more specifically, 'What is going on when bad things happen to good people?'.[3] A common and mistaken habit here is to think of creation as something which occurred in the past rather than as present process. God never stops creating. He sustains the creation and continues to create by redeeming and transforming. If we spend too much energy in scrutinizing and comparing explanations or theories of suffering we shall be too distracted to observe what is actually happening. For out of such observation hope can be born for ourselves and offered through us to others.

> "I cannot reconcile the images of tiny, deformed children with old men's eyes, in great pain, with what I am bound to believe of a loving, omnipotent Father. I will not assent to all this pain as anything but a manifest evil."[4]

These words carry weight as a protest against bland doctrines of divine providence and the assumption that God is always and everywhere in control of everything. But there must be some relation between God and anything we might call evil. Merely to insist that suffering is an evil does not explain it, any more than the story of Adam, Eve and the serpent explains how evil came into the world. It is often overlooked that the serpent was already evil.

In his analysis of the Book of Job, Kushner offers three statements which most people would like to believe:[3]

- God is all-powerful and causes everything which happens in the world. Nothing happens without his willing it
- God is just and fair, and stands for people getting what they deserve, so that the good prosper and the wicked are punished
- Job is a good person.

He goes on to comment:

> "As long as Job is healthy and wealthy, we can believe all three of those statements at the same time with no difficulty. When Job suffers, when he loses his possessions, his family and his health, we have a problem. We can no longer make sense of all three propositions together. We can now affirm any two only by denying the third."[3]

When we have met Job, when we have **been** Job we can no longer believe in an all-wise, all-powerful God who guarantees fair treatment and happy endings, who reassures us that everything happens for a reason.

Nevertheless the possibility can never be excluded that the lack of one kind of wholeness may open up other kinds not hitherto imagined. Here are some instances:

- A husband writes of his wife's last illness:
  "The suffering of a long and terminal illness is not all waste. Nothing that creates such tenderness can be all waste."[5]

- Someone dying from AIDS wrote:
  "I feel grateful that through my journey into my despair and anger and hopelessness I have become aware, I have been released into a sense of the massive

potential of life. It seems to me that this is the essence of everything - our potential for everything amidst nothing... Perhaps heaven and hell are sort of within us and we have the potential to live in heaven now - if we can go through the veil of anguish and tears that we have built up over the years."[6]

• A woman who has suffered from a severe bone disease for twenty years writes:

"Learning to live with the disorder as creatively as possible has in the end formed the person I am... I think I can say, without any trace of masochism, that the disease has indeed been a creative medium. I have tried to use the pain of it to remind me to try to focus on what is really important. And what is really important is adoration."[4]

This woman speaks also of being "open to pain", and of the corporate dimension of this process:

"I cannot describe the process very well, but I have found it to be one of somehow **absorbing darkness** - a physical or mental suffering of my own, or worse, of someone else - into my own person, my own body, or my own emotions. We have to allow ourselves to be open to pain. If we are able to do this, to act, as it were as blotting-paper for pain, without handing it on in the form of bitterness or resentment or of hurt to others - then somehow in some incomprehensible miracle of grace, some at least of the darkness may be turned to light."[4]

Thus a pain which on the surface appears to be isolated in the individual is found to be a means of another's healing. It is hinted here, though with no moralizing note, that in the most improbable circumstances we may find ourselves helping to create one another's lives through the medium of suffering. A complementary point is sometimes made about intercessory prayer as the empowering of the sufferer through the bearing and offering of pain on the sufferer's behalf. Such prayer can have this function but, equally, it can have more dubious functions, identified by someone ministering to people with AIDS:

"I learned that this ministry was not about bringing my package of the sacraments to people, but was about just being there, staying with the pain as it really was. It was about the hell of just staying there with no role and nothing to do, no goods to deliver. This was a very powerful transformation for me. I realized how often we ease our own feelings by doing something. We actually make ourselves feel better by saying, 'Let me say a prayer', because I have nothing else to say."[7]

This sense of identification with suffering attains another dimension in St Paul's claim:

"In my flesh I complete what is lacking in Christ's afflictions for the sake of his body, that is, the church." (Col.1.24 RSV)

What then of Jesus, of whom it is said "he learned obedience through his sufferings" (Heb.5.8)? This passage claims that the saving factor is Jesus' obedience, not his suffering as such. It is not, of course, denied that his obedience, like ours, involves suffering; but it is not Christian teaching that suffering is in itself redemptive. "One of the commonest Christian heresies is surely to glorify suffering as somehow 'good'." [4] The Letter to the Hebrews is not, however, a dogmatic statement to say that the purpose of **all** human suffering is the learning of obedience, though it does open up such a possibility for other people also.

Jesus' suffering on the cross was a chosen suffering in the sense that he did not have to be crucified:

> "The Father loves me because I lay down my life, to receive it back again. No one takes it away from me; I am laying it down of my own free will." (John 10.17-18)

The suffering is involved in his vocation. To choose and to see virtue in suffering as such would be masochistic. Of Jesus it is said that "for the sake of the joy that lay ahead of him, he endured the cross" (Heb.12.2). A central implication of his story is that the prospect of joy is a focus of hope to those who encounter unchosen suffering, for whom the choice is not whether to suffer, but what can be made of it.

When St Paul describes "a thorn in my flesh" (2 Cor.12.7), he indicates that strength is found in weakness. The unrelieved suffering is the raw material out of which strength emerges. The Bible's most comprehensive image of suffering comes in Paul's awesome picture of the whole creation groaning as if in the pangs of childbirth (Rom.8.22). This suggests that we shall all suffer until the Consummation, while offering no explanation of why the processes of creation must involve suffering as well as joy. We are simply left in no doubt that some forms of suffering are to be endured for the sake of a mysterious outcome still in the making.

This reflection immediately raises the first of many awkward questions which need to be faced in any serious consideration of suffering. While it is observable that suffering can awaken people to the reality of distress in others and promote compassionate identification with their anguish, the following key questions remain:

- what suffering, either my own or other people's, is to be lived with, accepted and transcended?

- what suffering is to be minimized or removed if possible?
- how can we tell the difference?

Other questions arise from the fact that some people seem to centre themselves on their suffering, while others do not. For example, a person with cystic fibrosis refused to be defined by her condition and always insisted that there was more of her than her illness; while someone else with a far less serious disorder never let other people forget it. Is this a matter of different suffering-thresholds, or is it more complex? Is a great deal of the suffering we so readily attribute to illness or external circumstances really to do with some inner disquiet or unresolved trauma which the symptomatic focus both expresses and masks? Are we helped to bear, and perhaps control, our experience by giving it the name of suffering, and so making it somehow more significant?

Further, being cured may paradoxically bring its own pain, because the patient who has been relieved of the distressing symptom or removed from the destructive context may now have to take some responsibility. This is hinted at by Jesus in his question to the man crippled for nearly 40 years: "Do you want to get well?" (John 5.6).

Case History

A twenty-year old man had severe pain caused by bone cancer. A few days later, when the pain had been relieved, he began to complain bitterly about disturbing dreams and hallucinations. These related to sudden death or the danger of it. Those caring for him felt that the pain had previously acted as a form of distraction or 'mental anodyne', preventing him from facing up to the anxieties and fears which his illness and deterioration might be expected to provoke.

In this and similar situations where severe physical pain seems to function as an anodyne, to control pain may substitute one form of suffering for another. How much suffering has to do with facing the unknown, or with clinging to known pain of body or mind rather than surrendering to the mystery? If the hospice is to be a safe place to suffer once physical symptoms have been relieved,[8] it is essential to recognize the subtle and complex ways in which different people suffer (see p 129).

Who is God for Job Today? [9]

Article 1 of the Thirty-Nine Articles of the Church of England pictures God as 'without body, parts or passions'. Implicit in this is the traditional Christian insistence that God is impassible (i.e. not subject to suffering). Is this claim symptomatic of a desire to distance what is not under our control, namely suffering? In other words, do we regard God as impassible because our image of perfection includes an absence of suffering?

A recent writer on AIDS makes a relevant observation:

"Particularly insidious is the sort of theodicy which is so intent on preserving God from all responsibility for suffering that it attributes the responsibility to the sufferer. In some contexts the so-called 'free will defence', the theory that all suffering is to be attributed to the free choices of moral agents, reads like a classic exercise in blaming the victim... The natural physical revulsion that we feel about suffering and death is turned into a moral revulsion, an imputation to the sufferer of moral failure for which they are being justly punished. By such a strategy it is possible to preserve both our own righteousness and God's, setting ourselves up as with divine authority against the ones 'contaminated' through their own fault." [10]

24

It is a short step from this attempt to preserve God from all responsibility for suffering to the exclusion of all suffering from God, despite the Bible's great range of images of a passible God (e.g. Jer.31.3; Hos.11.4,8; 14.4).

More specifically, a central strand of Christian tradition insists that God suffers only in the human suffering of Jesus on the cross:

> "The suffering of God is not eternal and infinite; it is human and limited and the same kind of suffering as that of Auschwitz or of cerebral meningitis." [11]

It has also been argued that God suffers, but only with the certainty of final victory. Against this it has to be pointed out that by this exclusion from God of one of the most acute forms of suffering, namely despair, "the whole enterprise of his solidarity with humanity seems to break down".[12] If despair is not to be found in God, why other forms of suffering?

These and similar forms of acknowledgement that God suffers are too limited to meet the contemporary insistence, particularly among those who work in hospices, that only a suffering God speaks to their experience:

> "My only real God is the suffering Father revealed in the sorrow of Christ." [13]

> "This cross is eternal. There was a cross in the heart of God before there was one planted outside Jerusalem."[14]

> "You who weep, come to this God, for he weeps".[15]

But the danger of this way of speaking is that it does not do justice to the otherness and transcendence of God, who then becomes perilously like an enlarged version of ourselves.[12]

The Fathers of the early Church resisted saying that God suffers because in their mental world suffering was associated with change, contingency and time; and change was seen as incompatible with perfection. We do not think as they did, but we may still be grateful for the note of caution, as a corrective to the tendency to picture God as changing and developing in the same way that we change and develop. The affirmation of God's involvement with us does not imply or depend on any such identification of his ways with ours.

Further, the idea that God does not suffer can be seen as a statement of hope for suffering humanity. It voices the conviction of faith that, however great and widespread our suffering, it is never the whole story, and therefore never an adequate way of defining a person or group. But this conviction will not necessarily be an apt communication to every sufferer.

It is the Cross that tells us that there is suffering in God:

> "The Lamb slain since the foundation of the world."
> (Rev.13.8)

If we claim that God suffers beyond the human suffering of the cross, it is important to stress that we cannot know exactly what we mean by this claim. The emphasis on a suffering God derives at least in part from a genuine desire to affirm the thorough-going involvement of God in all human suffering.[16] It is an insistence that God really cares, that God is really affected by his creatures' pain. But, if we are to let God be God, we would be wise to maintain a certain reticence about **how** God is thus involved. Such reticence must always be, and be seen to be, the product of modesty and awe before the *mysterium tremendum*, "the high and exalted One, who is enthroned for ever" (Isa.57.15).

References

1   Frankl VE. *Man's Search for Meaning.* Pocket Books,New York 1963.
2   Lewis CS. *A Grief Observed.* Faber & Faber, London1966.
3   Kushner HS. *When Bad Things Happen to Good People.* Avon, New York 1983.
4   Spufford M. *Celebration.* Collins Fount, London 1989.
5   Worsthorne P. Cries of anguish are the food of love. Sunday Telegraph, Sept 12, 1990, p 18.
6   Sheldrick N. In: Woodward J. *Embracing the Chaos: Theological Responses to AIDS.* SPCK, London 1990, p 21.
7   Randall D. In: Woodward J. *Embracing the Chaos: Theological Responses to AIDS.* SPCK, London 1990, p 71.
8   Stedeford A. Hospice: a safe place to suffer? *Palliative Medicine* 1987; **1**: 73-74.
9   Cox D. *Man's Anger and God's Silence: The Book of Job.* St Paul Publications, Middlegreen 1990.
10   Jantzen G. In: Woodward J. *Embracing the Chaos: Theological Responses to AIDS.* SPCK, London 1990, p 25.
11   McCabe H. Faith and reason. In: *The Independent.* October 7, 1989.
12   Ford DF. Book review. *Journal of Theological Studies* 1990; **42**: 316-318.
13   Studdert-Kennedy GA. *The Hardest Part.* Hodder & Stoughton, London 1918, p 10.
14   Gillet L. Does God suffer? *Sobornost* 1954; Summer: 112-120.
15   Hugo V. Quoted in Gillet L. Does God Suffer? *Sobornost* 1954; Summer: 112-120.
16   Fiddes PS. *The Creative Suffering of God.* Clarendon Press, Oxford 1988.

3 THEOLOGY OF WEAKNESS AND FAILURE

The Good News of Christ's teaching is that it abolishes everything that smacks of a "power deity".[1] The New Testament speaks of:

- "the Lamb slain since the foundation of the world" (Rev.13.8)
- the Messiah who rides a donkey and not a war-horse (Matt. 21.5)
- a kingdom in which the first shall be last and the last first (Mark 10.31)
- a Master who washes the feet of his disciples (John 13.4-5).

This shift in religious thought has been described as "so drastic that it could justly be compared to the Copernican revolution in astronomy".[2] However, the religious revolution has repeatedly been betrayed and the Christian God has been turned into a national or cultural power-symbol, as was the norm in pre-Christian cults.

Paradox

At the heart of the theology of weakness and failure, there is paradox. It finds expression in Paul: "Power is most fully seen in weakness... When I am weak, then I am strong" (2 Cor.12.9-10). Similarly, he expounds the doctrine of the Cross which is "sheer folly" to the "man of learning" and "subtle debater" (1 Cor.1.18 & 20). Yet, Christ crucified "is the power of God and the wisdom of God" (1 Cor.1.24).

As a proud Roman citizen (Acts 22.28), an arrogant Pharisee (Phil. 3.4-6) and a beneficiary of Greek education (Acts 17.24-28, 1 Cor. 15.33), Paul was familiar with the tools of power (political, religious and cultural). He had come to identify, however, with a community whose members were not, on the whole, drawn from the ranks of the powerful (e.g. 1 Cor.1.26), and whose leader died on a cross, a degrading death which Paul calls "the weakness of God" (1 Cor.1.25) in stark contrast to "the powers that rule the world" (1 Cor.2.8).

> "The God who is with us is the God who forsakes us (Mark 15.34). God lets himself be pushed out of the world on to the cross. He is weak and powerless in the world, and that is precisely the way, the only way, in which he is with us and helps us. Matt.8.17 ("He took our illnesses from us and carried away our diseases") makes it quite clear that Christ helps us, not by virtue of his omnipotence, but by virtue of his weakness and suffering".[3]

Method and Strategy of Jesus

A substantial amount of evidence in the New Testament reflects the view that a war is going on between good and evil (e.g. Eph.6.10-17, Rev.12.7-9). Christ has disarmed these cosmic powers and triumphed over them on the Cross (Col.2.14-15). It is instructive to note his method and strategy. If we look at the pattern of our Lord's life and ministry in, for example Mark's Gospel, at first glance all is 'go'. Jesus moves swiftly from one activity to the next. John's Gospel also reflects a sense of haste, since time is short (e.g. John 9.4). Jesus takes initiatives. In his wake people and circumstances are transformed. He is the man of action; taking the lead; in control.

Closer study reveals that Jesus also withdraws; retreats to the sea, hills, desert, or a friend's house. He depends on others, from borrowed stable to borrowed grave:

- he accepts loaves and fishes from a boy
- water from the woman at the well
- hospitality from Martha and Mary
- a donkey on which to ride into Jerusalem
- precious oil to anoint his head and feet
- transport on the Lake.

The rhythm of involvement and withdrawal, giving and receiving, serving and being served, characterizes his life and ministry. After his arrest, however, Jesus is no longer 'doing' but being 'done to'.[4] In John's Gospel, he has finished the work God gave him to do (John 17.4). Day is over; night has come (John 13.30). After Jesus is handed over to the authorities, he remains central to the story, but as recipient, not initiator. He has entered into his passion, and it is evident in the Gospel narratives that it is the passion and death of Jesus which are crucial. The Good News of Christ finds its focus in the cross. The 'saving work' of Christ is fulfilled when he 'does nothing'; he cannot do anything since his hands and feet are pierced and held by nails.

Mark records that when the centurion on duty at the cross saw how Jesus died, he said: "Truly this man was the Son of God" (Mark 15.39 RV). This affirmation from the centurion was evoked not by some breath-taking act of irresistible power and unarguable authority, but by our Lord's hanging on the cross.

The witness of the New Testament is, therefore, that the world's salvation was accomplished in weakness and seeming failure. This salvation is part of God's grand design, "namely, that the universe, everything in heaven and on earth, might be brought into a unity in Christ" (Eph.1.10). The work of

30

Christ, which fulfils the divine purpose, is described by Paul as a ministry of reconciliation, in which those who are committed to Christ are enlisted (2 Cor.5.18-19).

Implications for Discipleship

This ministry looks like an impossible assignment. Indeed, this was recognized by Jesus in his dialogue with the disciples after they sang the Passover hymn and went out to the Mount of Olives (Mark 14.26-31). He said to them, "You will all lose faith" (Mark 14.27).

On the face of it, our Lord's method seems extraordinary. When people we love face a tough assignment, we do all in our power to bolster their confidence by assuring them that they will handle it successfully. Jesus does the opposite. By doing so, does he not help to bring about the very failure which they hotly repudiated?

Jesus' comment begins to make sense, however, if placed in the context of a mission whose terms of reference are 'weakness and failure'. Jesus himself was about to 'fail' by being arrested and crucified. To identify with Jesus in his mission involved a willingness to fail with him.

Contemporary Perceptions of Success in Treating the Sick

In the context of the National Health Service, where both in doctors' training and in patients' expectations the emphasis is on clinical success,[5] a terminally-ill patient may have to take second place to patients whose illness can be cured. A patient who is getting stronger merits attention and treatment which holds out hope of success. But there can be no 'successful' treatment for a patient who grows inevitably weaker. Terminally-ill patients are going to die, and death is failure.

The theology of weakness and failure, however, invests a comatose patient with a status which is no lower than that accorded to a patient who is responding well to the curative skills of doctors, nurses and therapists. It could be said that a patient who is totally unable to help himself, who is utterly weak and has failed to respond to curative treatment, comes nearest of all to identification with the Saviour of the world.

This theology is instructive not only for an understanding of the status of a terminally-ill patient; but also for an understanding of the relationship to the patient of those who care for him. The carers are not to be seen in terms of masterly professionals, organizing and administering a programme for the patient which will lead to a successful conclusion. Medical and nursing staff fulfil a humbler role in which:

- 'being with' is more important than 'doing'
- a partnership of mutual understanding is developed
- caring does not have to be validated by cure
- carers are prepared to wait and watch.

Development and Renunciation

Teilhard de Chardin[6] wrote of 'The Divinisation of our Passivities'. He beautifully expounds the rhythm of the Christian life in which there is a delicate balance between development and renunciation, attachment and detachment. The will to live and the determination to realize fullest potential need to give place at the appropriate time to acceptance and surrender if growth into "mature manhood, measured by nothing less than the full stature of Christ" (Eph.4.13) is to be achieved.

Teilhard's exposition of 'The Divinisation of our Passivities' is preceded by his equally important section on 'The Divinisation of our Activities'. His finely-balanced phrases draw attention to the notorious difficulty facing all Christians in fulfilling their discipleship, that is, when to hold on and when to let go.

We face the same problem in hospice care. Should the terminally-ill patient be encouraged to 'fight' against his condition, or to submit to it? Teilhard wrote:

> "The hostile force that lays him low and disintegrates him, can become for him a loving principle of renewal, if he accepts it with faith while never ceasing to struggle against it".[6]

The carers cannot force acceptance on the patient's part. They, in turn, must wait and give that quality of creative attention which discerns when the required point is reached, and thereafter support the patient in his submission. So achievement will be attained in ceasing to strive to achieve, and "power comes to its full strength in weakness" (2 Cor.12.9).

> "When the signs of age begin to mark my body (and still more when they touch my mind); when the ill that is to diminish me or carry me off strikes from without or is born within me; when the painful moment comes in which I suddenly awaken to the fact that I am ill or growing old; and above all at that last moment when I feel I am losing hold of myself and am absolutely passive within the hands of the great unknown forces that have formed me; in all those dark moments, O God, grant that I may understand that it is you (provided only my faith is strong enough) who are painfully parting the fibres of my being in order to penetrate to the very marrow of my substance and bear me away within yourself."[6]

Final Verdict

In the final book of the Bible, Jesus is called "Amen" (Rev.3.14), a Hebrew word which may be used in two ways: 'It shall be' denoting resolution or 'Let it be' denoting consent. Paul says that we say 'Yes' to the promises of God, echoing the 'Yes' of Jesus:

> "That is why, when we give glory to God, it is through Christ Jesus that we say 'Amen'." (2 Cor.1.20)

The paradox is again apparent. Our resolve that the promises of God shall be fulfilled finds its most perfect expression in our ultimate surrender to their fulfilment. In learning 'not to do' and in accepting death at the last, we fulfil the purpose of our lives, as Jesus did in his cry from the Cross: "It is accomplished!" (John 19.30). To share this faith is to find the freedom wherewith Christ has set us free (Gal.5.1).

> "Free at last, free at last,
> Thank God A'mighty I'm free at last"
> (Words on Martin Luther King's memorial)

References

1   Bloch E. *Man on His Own.* Herder & Herder, New York 1970.
2   Macquarrie J. *Christian Hope.* Mowbray, London 1978.
3   Bonhoeffer D. *Letters and Papers from Prison.* SCM Press, London 1971.
4   Vanstone WH. *The Stature of Waiting.* Darton, Longman and Todd, London 1982.
5   Wilson M. *A Coat of Many Colours.* Epworth, London 1988.
6   Teilhard de Chardin P. *Le Milieu Divin.* Fontana, London 1967.

4 DEATH IN CHRISTIAN THOUGHT

"Fear not that your life shall come to an end, but rather that it shall never have a beginning."[1]

Death as Biological Fact

Death can be a terrible prospect, both for the dying person and the family. For hospice staff there is an unusual exposure to successive deaths with a cumulative effect upon beliefs, attitudes and values which can make and break.

All living creatures share the experience of birth and death. For human beings the solemn fact of death throws its shadow forward. We know we are mortal. Yet even 'earthenware jars' can hold the treasure of new life in Christ (2 Cor.4.7). Human understanding of death in nature has been influenced in Western culture by the biological work of Darwin and others. Anselm, following Paul (Rom. 5. 12-14), spells out the earlier view of death as a negative and punitive event:

"It is inconsistent with God's wisdom and justice to compel man to suffer death without fault, when he made him holy to enjoy eternal blessedness. It therefore follows that had man never sinned he never would have died."[2]

Teilhard de Chardin sums up the evolutionist view when he describes death as "the great lever in the upsurge of life".[3] Without death in nature on a massive scale, human beings

35

would not have been created. Death and life are intertwined. There are joys in life like sexuality and having children which owe their existence to death. Immortal beings would not require replacements.

Death may be understood as a gift from God because it is intrinsic to God's continuing creation and re-creation of the world. Death has its own lessons to teach about life. For example, death sets limits to biological life and gives it value. For many people death is simply the end. The place of death may become very important (as at Hillsborough football stadium in Sheffield). For Jesus death is an end to limitations of time and place. Identification with the self-offering of Jesus can transform our own outlook on death so that acceptance of its reality for ourselves may intensify our love of life. Death also renders us accountable for life to God. Nevertheless, in Western secular society death is a source of denial.[4] The actual experience of dying can be prolonged and destructive. Patients, families and those who care for them may suffer grievously.

Our humanity rebels against the negativities of death such as broken relationships, the aborted potential of young lives, the awful suffering:

> "Do not go gentle into that good night
> Old age should burn and rave at close of day
> Rage, rage against the dying of the light."[5]

Death on a global scale appals us. In one lifespan we have seen two world wars, the Holocaust, Hiroshima, famine in Ethiopia, genocide in Cambodia and other tragedies. But death is not always due to man's inhumanity to man. Children suffer because of congenital faults in the creative process.[6] And in hospices much suffering derives from the way we are created mortal. Life is both unfair and ugly, but there is also justice and beauty. Compassion and cruelty are interwoven in the world as we know it. And this is God's world. Some would say that the Fall of Man (Gen. 3) has caused the 'crooked timber of humanity'. Others would ask, "Who is God to have made such a world?"

Death as Social Event

"Who bends not his eare to any bell, which upon any occasion rings? But who can remove it from that bell, which is passing a peece of himselfe out of this world? No man is an Iland, entire of it selfe; every man is a peece of the continent, a part of the maine; if a clod bee washed away by the Sea, Europe is the lesse... any mans death diminishes me, because I am involved in Mankinde; And therefore never send to know for whom the bell tolls; It tolls for thee."[7]

Donne's writing presupposes a model of humanity similar to St Paul's description of the Church as the body of Christ (1 Cor.12.27). This view conflicts with Western individualism which makes of death an isolated tragedy over which other people grieve and from which they recover. Such a view of humanity denies death its potential for transformation of the bereaved.[8] In many cultures death is the occasion for a great family gathering. It is an opportunity for strengthening bonds of love both with the departed and with one another.

But Western secular cultures are enslaved to the fear of death:

"He who pretends to look on death without fear lies. All men are afraid of dying, this is the great law of sentient beings, without which the entire human species would soon be destroyed."[9]

We are a death-fearing society, and our understanding of health and healing is also captive to the fear of death. Consequently the practice of medicine and nursing is influenced by such social fears and expectations. The status and power of the doctor in hospital derives from his skill, real or imagined, to prevent death. Surveys of the work of hospital chaplains and of the expectations which patients and staff have of their work show that they are widely associated with the idea of death. Staff see a useful role for the chaplain more clearly in terminal illness than in any other situation.[10]

But in Christian thought, as in a number of other religions, the fear of death may be borne in hope. Certainly the dying individual shrinks from an unknown future, but also hopes for release into a fuller relationship with God. Death is also a corporate experience through which the whole family (kin and hospice staff) may or may not grow nearer to God in their daily lives.[11] We are not simply spectators of death, we are always also participants: "any mans death diminishes me".

Death as Symbol

Death may be spoken of in two ways. A scientist speaks of a biological process or event which terminates existence. A poet, on the other hand, uses the word death as a symbol to convey the reality itself. The word points with sharp imagery to decay and ending in personal life, in body, mind, feeling or morality of individual or community.

> "Is it not strange that men can die
> Before their bodies do,
> And women's souls fade from their eyes?
> 'Tis strange, but it is so."[12]

In the Bible the word death is used both biologically and symbolically. "And there was Sisera lying dead, with the

38

tent-peg in his temple" (Jud.4.23) is a factual statement. "Your brother here was dead and has come back to life; he was lost and has been found" (Luke 15.32) is a metaphorical image of living death both for the prodigal son in a distant country, and for the father waiting at home. There are living deaths worse than biological death.

Psychologists, sociologists, historians and theologians have always made use of poetic imagery to convey the reality of death as a loss of quality in our individual or common life, rather than death merely as a loss of quantity of days of existence. These living deaths involve a diminishment of health, such as a maiming of body or self, a withering of humanity, a denial of participation by exclusion or banishment, a loss of meaning through oppression. Such things can be deadly to human potential. These things spell death. People may die amid plenty, or may live fully though dying. In Christian thought and practice there is a conflict of outlook with the common belief, based on fear, that biological death is the worst thing that can happen to a person. Being children of a culture, many Christians absorb this value which moulds their outlook and motivates their behaviour:

> "Don't let the world around you squeeze you into its own mould, but let God re-mould your minds from within." (Rom. 12.2) [13]

Some live dying; better to die living.

Real Life and Real Death

In the Old Testament, life and blessing are obedience to the commandments of God and keeping the covenant of love, meaning right-relatedness. Disobedience is death and curse. Israel is given a free choice (Deut.30.15-20).

In the New Testament the words 'life' and 'Kingdom of God' are interchangeable (Mark 9.43 45 & 47). Christ is the source of true life. To become alive in Him involves a new birth. We become alive as creatures in a birth from the water of the womb; we become alive as children of God (John 1.12) in a birth by the Spirit (John 3.3-8).

In Christian thought the emphasis is on life:

- life in Christ
- risen life
- fullness of life
- right-relatedness to God, neighbour and self
- salvation
- *shalom*
- kingdom life.

The priority given to this quality of life is not lost in the face of biological death. Indeed biological death and the care of the dying are all to be seen in the context of life, because the death of Jesus has reversed human perspectives. Life is freed through death.

Although all human beings are made in the image and likeness of God (Gen.1), there is a sense in which we are dead until we are re-born:

> "But God is rich in mercy, and because of his great love for us, he brought us to life with Christ when we were dead because of our sins; it is by grace you are saved." (Eph.2.4)

We pass from this death by a complete change of heart (*metanoia*) which is a gate into the Kingdom of God. This re-birth is symbolized by the sacrament of Baptism. It was Jesus who first spoke of his own death as a baptism, and said that his disciples would share it (Mark 10.38). Baptism, especially total immersion, uses the imagery of natural birth from water to air (Rom.6.3-11).

Christianity is often so tamed, however, that to use the word 'death' of entry into the Christian life seems a mockery. But the early Church's preparation for baptism during Lent involved the catechumens in a painful identification with the death of Christ. Repeated exorcisms were felt to be necessary to banish the old evil ways of life and bring death to their old beliefs, values and lifestyle in readiness for the growth of the resurrection life within them.

In Christian thought, repentance/conversion/baptism is an identification with the death of Jesus. We are baptized into his death (Rom.6.3). It is a death to our old life and the beginning of a new life in Christ (John 11.25). We are already risen people who have died the death that matters and entered everlasting life. At this point a self-offering is made to God for the service of the kingdom. This is what fullness of humanity really means. This is how God made human beings to be. Identification with the self-offering of Jesus means that we can live daily with the conscious knowledge of our mortality and are freed from the unconscious fear of death so characteristic of Western secular society. This gives life a quality which biological death cannot destroy. Biological death of body is therefore the ending of limitation, a door into a new form of being, a total surrender to the unknown, with faith in God: "Father, into your hands I commit my spirit" (Luke 23.46).

Lovelessness, self-withholding, alienation and all that is meant by sin are lived patterns of death, the real deaths of the human spirit blind to God in our midst. It is not biological death we are to fear, it is the living death and corruption of sin (Luke 12.4-5). And it is sin which blinds us to the nature of death so that it appears as the end. Transformation from the old life to the new demands both a self-offering and, daily thereafter, a painful series of changes in perceptions, attitudes and values which can well be described as a series of deaths through which renewal of life comes. The Christian life is a continual passion.

The acid test of this real life is a very practical one, namely its quality of love:

> "We know we have crossed over from death to life because we love our fellow-Christians." (1 John 3.14)

Jesus died as he lived. He loved his own to the end (John 13.1; 15.13). His death sums up the whole truth about his life. His passion did not begin when they nailed his hands and feet. There were the hours and days and years before the crucifixion. He had to struggle with temptation, and to choose between home and work, family and friends, privacy and publicity, life and death. There were times of excited acclamation and bitter rejection. All this involved passion before he ever freely set his face to go to Jerusalem, and the disciples were afraid, but not for the first time. His death was the final sacrifice and the sacrament of his whole lifestyle; self-offering to the Father in work for the kingdom.

The New Testament states that human fulfilment is to be with Christ both now and in the realm beyond death (Eph. 1.10). The crucial point is not biological death (however momentous an experience this is) but baptism/conversion in faith. That is, we have been identified with Christ in his death and resurrection (Rom. 6.3-4). The Christ who died and rose will include in his final triumph those who are already risen persons, despite the fact that they may have died.

> "Death has no crucial significance in the calendar of the new life. Here the only relevant moments are Baptism and the *Parousia*." [14]

The *parousia* is the completion of God's purpose, the End (*Eschaton*), the fulfilment of the Kingdom of God; what the whole universe now groans its way towards (Rom. 8.22). Our attention, as Christians, is not upon death, nor even beyond it on a post-death existence, but is given to God's continuous creation and recreation of the world here and now. From this perspective of new life in Christ:

"O Death, where is your victory? O Death, where is your sting?" (1 Cor.15.55)

The history of Christian thought about death is a struggle to hold in tension the Christian calendar of a self-offered life (life in Christ from new birth to the End) with the reality of suffering and the dissolution of our existing pattern of being human. Although in Christian thought death is no longer seen as the end, the hospice is a crucible of everyday life where the human experience of biological death leads through Gethsemane. To grasp and live this truth often takes a lifetime. And what of those who pass the acid test of love, but belong to other Faiths or none? Jesus said, "You will recognize them by their fruit" (Matt. 7.15-23; Matt. 25.31-46).

Death and Judgement

In the gospel narratives, Jesus speaks of hell on several occasions (e.g. Matt. 10.28; 23.33; 25.31-46; Mark 9.42-48; Luke 16.19-31). These statements cannot be ignored, yet are incredible to many Christians if taken at face value. They contrast starkly with the proclamation of 'Good News', and other statements by Jesus (Mark 3.35; 10.45) and by St Paul (1 Cor.15.22; Col.1.19-20).

Christians working in hospices tend to become 'universalist' in outlook (see p 230). Absolute 'universalism', however, is as misguided as the narrow view of the 'fundamentalist'. The possibility that there may be some who continue to place themselves outside the love of God must remain:

> "There are only two kinds of people in the end: those who say to God: 'Thy will be done', and those to whom God says, in the end: '**Thy** will be done.' All that are in hell, choose it. Without that self-choice there could be no hell." [15]

> "We used to comfort ourselves by saying that while we perhaps had to believe that hell existed we didn't have to hold that anyone ever went there. In speaking thus we had forgotten Jesus, and by implication everyone else, for his story is ours: through hell to heaven. You have to have forgotten not only Jesus but a great deal of your own experience to be able to doubt either hell or its inhabiting. Equally you have to be in full flight from present reality to place hell firmly and exclusively after death, and to picture it as a sealed-off alternative to heaven. Such literalism misses the meaning." [16]

Although for some hell conveys an image of final rejection and destruction, others speak of the harrowing of hell, 'Fear not to enter hell, for Christ your Saviour has harrowed it'. Hell, the projected place where we put all the evil with which we cannot cope in ourselves or others, is thus brought near, reactivated within us, and harrowed in preparation for harvest.

Death and Resurrection

The death of Jesus on Good Friday is an unspeakable event. Treachery, denial and flight revealed to all the disciples the truth about themselves and their relationship to Jesus. His death left them shocked, abandoned, and hopeless (Luke 24.13-32). They felt let down.

But the death of Jesus is the key to life. The whole meaning of life is decisively re-interpreted by the death of Jesus. We have described above the personal and social effects of the fear of death characteristic of Western secular cultures. Jesus puts this flight from death into reverse.[17] He lived with an unrepressed awareness of death, and always for him incarnation has appeared as a limitation beyond which his powers would be released for the whole world. So he was able to set his face to go to Jerusalem:

"For the sake of the joy that lay ahead of him, he endured the cross, ignoring its disgrace." (Heb.12.2)

He therefore sees death as both desirable ("It is in your interest that I am leaving you. If I do not go, the advocate will not come, whereas if I go, I will send him to you" John 16.7) and dreadful (Mark 14.32-36). He lives and dies in this spirit.

The resurrection on Easter morning could not prettify the suffering of the cross, nor erase the event as if it had never been. The cross revealed the extent of God's love and passionate identification with humankind, and the source of God's forgiveness, not only for the disciples, but for all. Sin, which sees death as the end, is not the final word: "[Jesus] has set it aside, nailing it to the cross" (Col.2.14). God is shown to be transforming the creation by suffering; life is given through death.

Christian hope is founded upon this abiding relationship with God. It is a hope both in the present, when union with God is given through the gift of the Holy Spirit, and in the future, because death cannot destroy the gift of God's love. "For here we have no lasting city" (Heb.13.14). Yet, having nothing, we possess all things.[18]

Death and Discipleship

When people become aware that they have been wrong, the changes and learning which follow are painful. The effects are closely similar to the stages of a bereavement.[19] The 'death' and consequent bereavement through which catechumens had to pass on their way to baptism symbolized their life through death with Christ.

Today we need similarly to address the deep change of values involved in preparation for church membership. An intellectual approach alone is not enough.[20] The new learning of a conversion is a Calvary as old perceptions die out and transformation of the person takes place (Rom. 12.2). Then our acceptance of death as desirable, even if dreaded, frees us from slavery to fear (Rom. 8.15; 2 Tim. 1.7).

The human response to loss of many kinds (such as redundancy, bereavement or an injury to a sportsman) is like dying to the old life and rising to new life. The great negativities of life may prove to be enhancements. In these events the fingerprints of a dying/rising God at work may be recognized. Those who share in the life-through-death changes of growth in daily life may also see in the face of their biological death a familiar pattern, and will already have learned to endure, to face the unknown with courage, and to expect with joy a gift of new life through death whose nature cannot be foreseen.

References

1   Newman JH. Source unknown.
2   Anselm. *Cur Deus Homo.* In: *Ancient and Modern Library of Literature. Book II.* Griffith, Farran and Browne, London 1889, p 62.
3   Teilhard de Chardin P. *The Phenomenon of Man.* Collins, London 1959.

4   Pattison E. *The Experience of Dying*. Prentice Hall, London 1977.
5   Thomas D. *Collected Poems 1934-1952*. Dent, London 1966, p 159.
6   Spufford M. *Celebration*. Collins Fount, London 1989.
7   Donne J. *Complete Verse and Selected Prose*. Hayward J (ed). Nonesuch Press, London 1972: Devotions XVII.
8   Harvey NP. *Death's Gift*. Epworth, London 1985.
9   Rousseau J-J. (1712-1778). *Julie or The New Eloise*. Bell, Dixon and Elliot, Edinburgh 1773.
10   Wilson JM. A Ghetto for Death. In: *The Hospital - A Place of Truth*. University of Birmingham, Birmingham 1971, p 114.
11   Wilson JM. Death and Society. In: Millard DW (ed). *Religion and Medicine 3*. SCM Press, London 1976, p 52-71.
12   Turner WJ. 'Reflection'. In: Yeats WB (ed). *The Oxford Book of Modern Verse 1892-1935*. Oxford University Press, Oxford 1936: no. 269.
13   Phillips JB. *The New Testament in Modern English for Schools*. Bles Collins, London 1959.
14   Robinson JAT. Preaching Death. In: *On Being the Church in the World*. SCM Press, London 1960, p 129.
15   Lewis CS. *The Great Divorce*. Geoffrey Bles, London 1945, p 66.
16   Harvey NP. *The Morals of Jesus*. Darton, Longman & Todd, London 1991: p 107.
17   Moore S. *The Inner Loneliness*. Darton, Longman and Todd, London 1982: p 97-99.
18   Kung H. *Eternal Life?* Collins Fount, London 1985.
19   Colston LG. *Judgement in Counselling*. Abingdon Press, Nashville 1969, p 50.
20   Wilson M. *A Coat of Many Colours*. Epworth, London 1988.

SECTION II : HEALING

5 THE CHURCH'S MINISTRY OF HEALING

The phrase 'the Church's ministry of healing' is said to have been used in print for the first time only in 1881.[1] From the time of Christ until the fourth century, however, physical healing was a common concomitant of the proclamation of the Gospel.[2] Physical healing became less common after Christianity was made legal within the Roman empire in 313 AD. Miraculous cures have continued to be associated with a number of individuals, however, including the well-known preachers George Fox (1624-1691), John Wesley (1703-1791) and, more recently, Padre Pio (1887-1968).

Lack of expectation within the Church generally concerning physical healing was enhanced by Descartes in the first half of the seventeenth century. Cartesian dualism stressed separateness between body and soul. The body was assigned to the care of the medical profession and the soul to the care of the Church. It was perhaps not surprising, therefore, that a re-awakening of interest in a 'ministry of healing' in the nineteenth century should emphasize inexplicable rather than medically explicable healing.

The early part of the twentieth century saw the emergence in Britain of a number of initiatives aimed at encouraging cooperation between the Church and the medical profession, but which also encouraged belief in cure through prayer and the sacraments.[2] The following were among the early organizations to be established:

- Guild of Health (1904)
- Society of Emmanuel (1905) which became Divine Healing Mission (1933)
- Guild of St Raphael (1915)
- Crowhurst Home of Healing (1928)
- Order of St Luke (1947)
- Churches' Council of Healing (1944) which became Churches' Council of Health and Healing (1970)
- Dorothy Kerin Community and Church of Christ the Healer, Burrswood (1948).

Interest continues and more than 50 organizations and Christian healing centres now exist in Britain alone.[3]

The Ministry of Healing

Health is not just the absence of disease but a positive state of 'right-relatedness' to God and of dependence on him (see chapter 7). This can come about only through the harmonious evolution of a fourfold relationship:[4]

- to the good earth beneath one's feet (one's physical environment)
- to other people (one's living and human environment)
- to oneself (through a right ordering of one's own inner and complex existence)
- to God (the source of all one's being).

The Church's ministry of healing will therefore:

- be an integral part of the life of every Christian community
- be concerned with the journey towards right-relatedness with the environment, neighbour, self and God, not simply with physical cure

- acknowledge the work of nurses, doctors and other health-care professionals as partners in God's work of healing.

The components of the Church's ministry of healing are therefore many and varied. Broadly speaking they can be divided into sacramental and non-sacramental means. Sacramental means include:

- Baptism
- Holy Communion
- confession and absolution
- anointing
- laying on of hands
- deliverance.

These have been described elsewhere.[2,5,6,7,8] Non-sacramental means include:

- friendship
- forgiveness, acceptance and affirmation
- active listening,[9] counselling and psychotherapy
- nursing and medical care
- prayer
- healing of emotions and memories.

The healing of damaged emotions and of destructive memories ('inner healing') involves Christian counselling and prayer which focuses on the power of the Holy Spirit to bring healing.

In this context, damaged emotions relate to extreme feelings about personal unworthiness, sensitiveness and fear of failure.[10] Destructive memories frequently stem from repressed unresolved anger about emotional hurts in the past (e.g. sexual abuse as a child by a parent).[11]

The healing of memories does not erase the memories, indeed it commonly serves to bring them into consciousness, but their meaning is changed and their sting withdrawn. The memories become accepted and integrated into the person's total life. The basis of this healing is forgiveness - forgiving the person responsible for the hurts, even to "seventy times seven" (Matt. 18.22).

While both damaged emotions and destructive memories may be helped by psychotherapy, the process of healing can be hastened by prayer. The Holy Spirit may bring a buried experience into consciousness, or help a known problem to be faced and borne or resolved. Although all of us have emotional hang-ups and hurts from the past, many achieve progressive inner healing through friendship and active listening, as well as within a supportive worshipping community and sharing in the Eucharist.

Miracles

Inadequate documentation and follow-up bedevils those who concentrate on inexplicable healing.[12,13] It is generally accepted, however, that there is sufficient evidence to assert that inexplicable physical healings still occur.[14-17] At Lourdes in France, there has been a medical bureau for more than a century. Of over 1000 cases of physical healing examined between 1918 and 1957, 54 have been accepted by both doctors and priests as undoubted miracles.[2]

Inexplicable healings seem to be more commonly associated with a select group of individuals who have a special charisma or gift of healing.[18,19] Such wonders may or may not be miracles.[17] Miracles are uncommon and sporadic, and their purpose goes beyond physical restoration (Luke 5.24). For an inexplicable healing to be a miracle, it must: [20,21]

- be a happening that causes wonder
- be a sign pointing to God at work
- invite people to respond to God.

Miracles are unpredictable and mysterious, but they may be understood by faith to be revelations of God's love for the creation, and visible signs of the presence of the Kingdom of God growing secretly.

The power of prayer to heal receives strong testimony today.[22] We can pray to God for healing but cannot be sure how God will answer. We can always pray wholeheartedly 'Thy will be done' because God has revealed his purposes for the world through Jesus, and we can rely on the sovereignty and grace of God.

But to raise the expectations of cure for a dying person can be terribly wrong. God often blesses a person whether physically healed or not.

Case Histories 1 & 2

Two middle-aged women asked for the laying on of hands. Both were unable to walk because of poliomyelitis, and were confined to wheel-chairs. The first was a housewife with a family. She received the laying on of hands from an Anglican priest. Two days later, she awoke in the morning with a feeling of 'pins and needles' in her legs, and so hung them over the side of the bed. She tested them on the floor and found that she was able to walk a few paces. The front door bell rang, and she staggered to the door and opened it. The postman was amazed to see her standing. She recovered her power to walk and devoted her spare time to setting up and running a club for handicapped people. For the rest of her life she remained a great advocate for the Church's ministry of healing.

The second woman was a missionary who worked in a School of Technology. She received the laying on of hands from an Anglican priest at a service of Holy Communion. She noticed no physical changes in her legs but commented, "It's a good thing I can continue my vocation sitting". She returned in her wheel-chair to the Christian school overseas and continued to work there as a laboratory technician.

The work of God in the world was continued by both these women. Why God cured one and not the other is a mystery before which we stand humbled. We experience the same mystery in God's providence: one person may be saved dramatically from a disaster, but another person unaccountably suffers. As one person said, "God gives minimum protection but maximum support".[23]

The interaction of mind and body through the 'neuro-endocrino-immune cycle' is well documented,[24,25] and provides a possible scientific understanding for some physical healing through non-medical means, including miracles. This same cycle of positive interaction probably underlies the well-recognized 'placebo' response whereby, in many diseases, an inert medicine will bring definite benefit in about one-third of cases.[26,27,28]

Disparate Views

Significantly different views are held about the Church's ministry of healing. Two streams of thought which have been prominent in recent years have been termed **charismatic** and **revived Pentecostalism**. These are described elsewhere.[7] For many people, charismatic renewal has been their point of entry into the Church's healing ministry, whether as recipients or as instruments of healing. There is no reason in principle why strong emphasis on charismatic gifts should conflict with the ethos of the hospice. But in practice difficulties can arise, particularly with those who:

- have little theology of suffering and dying
- fail to acknowledge God's work in nursing and medicine, and the other health-care professions
- are unwilling to tackle multi-professional study and face possible conflicts.

Revived Pentecostalism resembles the Holiness and Pentecostalist movements of the 1920s and 1930s, in that emphasis is given to possession by demons and to 'signs and wonders' in association with the proclamation of the gospel.[29,30] While apparently bringing God nearer, **revived Pentecostalism** in reality may push him away into the supernatural:

> "The more God is met in special experiences, the easier it is mentally to 'locate' him outside of the ordinary. When this happens our spiritual life is kept alive by 'signs and wonders' and is shaken when we are deprived of them. To seek God only in the supernatural is to deny the message of Christmas and Cross. It removes all hope and comfort from the unhealed sick because they are led to believe that God has forsaken them, rather than is suffering with them. It is the pagans who locate God exclusively in wonders; for Christians he is 'ordinarily in the ordinary', i.e. where we need him most".[7]

A Ministry of Healing for the Uncured and Dying?

The danger of making physical cure the central emphasis in the Church's ministry of healing is evident not only in a hospice, but also in a general hospital:

> "As a full-time hospital chaplain... I am becoming increasingly concerned about some of the teaching

regarding the Christian healing ministry which I frequently find is being presented, especially to some of the terminally ill patients with whom I come into contact. In fact it seems to me that there is an almost fanatical emphasis on physical healing, and that no matter how serious the condition of the patient, faith in God is all that is necessary for that person to be restored to radiant health. Now, I am not denying that faith is important, although I know of some cases where remarkable healing has taken place when there has been little or even no faith; neither am I saying that miraculous healings do not take place, I know they do. I am saying, however, that healing is not as simple as some people make it out to be, and that God heals in different ways; and the way is His choice, not ours."[31]

Case History 3

WT, a 29 year-old married man with three young children, was found to have an inoperable brain tumour. Two and a half years later, he was referred to a hospice because of epileptic fits and family tensions. He was admitted on several occasions to provide respite for the family. Among the forms of support open to WT and his family was the local parish church. In due course, Mr & Mrs T requested that the children should be baptized. Subsequently, however, Mrs T threatened to call off the Baptism service because she could not cope any more with prayers for W's healing which on this occasion would have been offered in his presence. The hospice staff asked the vicar to consider prayers for peace of mind instead. The Baptism went ahead and the next two months were perhaps the best throughout the whole devastating illness - then already in its fourth year.

It could be claimed that Mrs T's distress about the proposed prayers for healing stemmed from too narrow an understanding of the meaning of the word. Yet, it is surely incumbent on those who hold healing services to use language that those attending can understand without too much explanation. In this case 'peace of mind' was a wholly appropriate focus for the prayers of the Church, and was agreed between vicar, hospice staff and family.

Case History 4

A 42 year-old married man with two young children had recurrent cancer. Six months previously he had had a remission induced by chemotherapy, but the disease had relapsed again and he was now close to death. He was depressed and distressed about the anticipated separation from his wife and children. Some friends decided to pray for a miracle and arranged an overnight vigil of prayer. The local vicar was not sure whether it was appropriate and did not participate. The wife was quite sure - quite sure that the miracle was six months ago, and that it was wrong to continue to pray for cure. She was upset and angry at the action of the friends but felt powerless to stop the vigil. Two days later she told the hospice physician of her distress. He agreed that praying for cure was inappropriate, and that efforts should be re-directed towards praying for the miracle of a peaceful death. With the wife's permission, the doctor telephoned the vicar to arrange a meeting to talk matters over. This took place the next day and, subsequently, the vicar spoke to the leader of the praying friends. About 30 minutes later, the patient experienced a severe central chest pain caused by a cardiac arrhythmia. His condition deteriorated dramatically and he died in the early hours of the next day.

This account suggests that prayer can never be neutral in its effects because it operates at both psychological and spiritual levels. The inference is that praying for a miracle prevented this man from achieving an inner peace and from dying. In other words, the prayers added to and prolonged his suffering. This testimony to possible negative effects of prayer is not unique.[32]

This raises a number of ethical issues which, as yet, appear not to have been faced by pray-ers who bombard God with specific requests for third parties. That the person prayed for should agree to the content of the prayers being offered would seem to be an important consideration. The alternative is presumably to be non-specific, and simply 'offer up' the person to God for blessing (Matt.6.7-8).

Case History 5

HC was a 23 year-old married woman with a past history of cancer of the colon treated by surgery. She was referred to a hospice because of abdominal pain. Investigations confirmed recurrent intra-abdominal cancer. She deteriorated visibly over the next few months, and was cared for mostly at home by her husband and mother.

For the last four months of her life she was visited regularly by a clergyman who had been introduced by some friends at work. He prayed regularly for her healing. Two months before she died, the clergyman made provisional arrangements for her to attend a healing service some 30 miles away because he believed she should still 'claim' physical healing. At the time she was housebound and largely bedbound. Almost at the last minute she declined to go. Despite this, he continued to visit her. Several weeks later, just a few days before she died, she said to a visiting nurse, "I am so frightened. Tell me how to die! I don't know how to die!"

If the Church's ministry of healing is to do with "Jesus Christ meeting you at the point of your need",[33] this is a tragic example of a false ministry. Regular faithful ministry failed totally to help this young woman prepare for her death. Because everybody dies eventually (including Lazarus), the ministry of healing must be comprehensive enough to encompass preparation for death. Contemporary evidence suggests that all too often this is not the case.

Misconceptions

Other examples of a misunderstanding of the Church's ministry of healing appear in medical journals from time to time:

Case History 6

A woman in her 30s with myxoedema (atrophy of the thyroid gland) was well-maintained for many years on thyroxine tablets. After attending a healing service at her parish church, she decided she had no need of her hormone replacement therapy. Over the next few months she developed a florid psychotic illness caused by thyroxine deficiency. Eventually she was admitted to a psychiatric hospital and the thyroxine restarted. She made a steady recovery and remained stable thereafter.[34]

Case History 7

A 52 year-old man had been taking anticonvulsants to control epilepsy for 25 years. He had been well-controlled for some 10 years and was employed as a millhand driller. After consulting a faith healer, he stopped all medication. He began to have fits both at work and at home, one resulting in injury. He lost his job and the firm lost a skilled and valued employee. The man blamed himself for his seizures, believing that they resulted from impure thoughts.[13]

It is clear that in some people's minds there are serious and potentially dangerous misconceptions about the Church's ministry of healing on the one hand, and disease and medical treatment on the other. In relation to the former, common misconceptions include:

- cure inevitably follows faith
- suffering is always contrary to God's will
- death is a disaster
- sickness is always caused by sin
- modern medicine has superseded the Church's ministry of healing
- only the specially gifted can practise the Church's ministry of healing
- the Church's ministry of healing is separate from its other work
- physical cure is all that matters
- sacramental ministries such as communion of the sick and anointing presage death
- medically inexplicable healing is more wonderful than healing brought about by medical means.

Some of the more common misconceptions about disease and medical treatment which give rise to unfounded claims in connection with the Church's ministry of healing include:

- ignorance about the natural history of many disorders
- a sequence of events assumed to be cause and effect
- a belief that doctors can give accurate predictions of life expectancy.

These have been discussed fully elsewhere.[35,36]

A Challenge for the Future

A basis for future endeavour may follow some of the suggestions made in the Report of the Anglican Lambeth Conference in 1988[37] and in the Report of the Christian Medical Commission of the World Council of Churches.[38] Any future Christian mission in the world would be founded on Christ's injunction to his disciples to preach the Kingdom and heal the sick (Luke 9.2). World-wide consultations with members of Christian congregations have suggested that this mission is best carried out when:

- the ministry of healing is a regular part of the ministry of every congregation in its own locality
- intercessory prayer by members of every congregation is encouraged in the light of Our Lord's promise about the efficacy of corporate prayer (Matt. 18.19)
- the laying on of hands with prayer is used by both clergy and other members of the congregation
- oil for anointing the sick is blessed and priests are encouraged to make this anointing a regular part of their ministry to the sick
- counselling concerned with inner healing and the healing of relationships is encouraged, and provision is made for the ministry of absolution and the assurance of forgiveness
- ministries of deliverance from demonic possession are provided where this is needed in cooperation, where appropriate, with doctors
- centres for the ministry of healing are established both for ministry to the sick and for the teaching, training and support of health-care workers and others engaged in this ministry locally

- the work of doctors, nurses, other professional carers and volunteers is recognized as part of the Church's
- ministry of healing, and cooperation is encouraged between all involved in the care of the sick
- medical research is encouraged and also the study of related ethical issues
- a just distribution of resources and personnel is sought so that all nations and all sections of the community may receive adequate health care
- the sick and disadvantaged (e.g. drug addicts and sufferers from AIDS) are embraced as part of the fellowship of the Church
- the work of medical missions throughout the world is supported as an important part of the Church's total ministry
- hospices for the terminally ill are established and appropriate ministry for the dying and their families is provided; this will need to include home visiting services and counselling in regard to the continuance or discontinuance of life-support systems in those who are dying
- both in matters of birth and death, medicine gives full respect to strengthening family relationships, giving thanks to God for the gift of life
- due regard is given to quality of life through the conservation of planet Earth in wholesome methods of agriculture, good conditions of work and housing, and a fair distribution of wealth.

This list is a comprehensive aid to perspective. But it must not be translated into rules of thumb, in an attempt to control or deny the irreducible mystery of the particular and ever-new encounter in which healing either occurs or does not.

References

1   Wilkinson J.   *Health & Healing: Studies in New Testament Principles and Practice*. Handsel, Edinburgh 1980.

2   Maddocks M.   *The Christian Healing Ministry* (2nd Edition). SPCK, London 1990.

3   *Residential and Day Centres of Christrian Healing*. Churches' Council for Health and Healing. London 1990.

4   Neill S. *Bible Words and Christian Meanings*. SPCK, London 1970, p 33.

5   Wilson M. *The Church is Healing*. SCM Press, London 1964.

6   Lambourne RA. *Community, Church and Healing*. Arthur James, Evesham 1963 & 1987.

7   Richards J. *The Question of Healing Services*. Darton, Longman & Todd, London 1989.

8   Richards J. *But Deliver Us From Evil*. Darton, Longman & Todd, London 1974.

9   Long A. *Listening*. Darton, Longman and Todd, London 1990.

10   Seamands DA. *Healing for Damaged Emotions*. Victor Books, Wheaton, 1981 and Scripture Press, Amersham-on-the-Hill 1986.

11   Seamands DA. *Healing of Memories*. Victor Books, Wheaton 1985 and Scripture Press, Amersham-on-the-Hill 1986.

12   Rose L. Some aspects of paranormal healing. *British Medical Journal* 1954; ii: 1329-1333.

13   Smith DM. Safety of faith healing. *Lancet* 1986; i: 621.

14   Frost HW. *Miraculous Healing*. Zondervan, Grand Rapids 1979.

15   Gardner R. Miracles of healing in Anglo-Celtic Northumbria as recorded by the Venerable Bede and his contemporaries: a reappraisal in the light of twentieth century experience. *British Medical Journal* 1983; **287**: 1927-1933.

16   Gardner R. *Healing Miracles: A Doctor Investigates*. Darton, Longman and Todd, London 1986.

17   Lewis D. *Healing: Fiction, Fantasy or Fact?* Hodder & Stoughton, London 1989.

18   Arnold DM. *Dorothy Kerin: Called by Christ to Heal*. Hodder & Stoughton, London 1965.

19   Smith F. *God's Gift of Healing*. New Wine Press, Chichester 1986.

20   Richardson A. *The Miracle Stories of the Gospels*. SCM Press, London 1941.

21   Melinsky MAH. *Healing Miracles*. Mowbray, London 1968.

22 Hollenweger WJ. Healing through Prayer: superstition or forgotten Christian tradition? *Theology* 1989; **92**: 166-174.

23 Coffin WS. My son beat me to the grave. *Thanatos* 1989; Spring: 20-21.

24 Antoni MH. Neuroendocrine influences in psychoimmunology and neoplasia: a review. *Psychology and Health* 1987; **1**: 3-24.

25 Baker GHB. Psychological factors and immunity. *Journal of Psychosomatic Research* 1987; **31**: 1-10.

26 Lindahl O, Lindwall L. Is all therapy just a placebo effect? *Metamedicine* 1982; **3**: 255-259.

27 Editorial. Shall I please? *Lancet* 1983; **ii**: 1465-1466.

28 Davidson P. Placebo response in medicine: the concepts. *New Ethicals* 1977; Sept: 23-28.

29 Wimber J. *Power Evangelism*. Hodder & Stoughton, London 1985.

30 Wimber J. *Power Healing*. Hodder & Stoughton, London 1986.

31 Holman H. Hospital chaplain on faith healing. *Chrism* 1990; **26 (10)**: 1.

32 Wilson J, Wilson M. Personal communication.

33 Maddocks M. *Twenty Questions About Healing*. SPCK, London 1988.

34 Coakley DV & McKenna GW. Safety of faith healing. *Lancet* 1986; **i**: 444.

35 Archbishops' Commission. *The Church's Ministry of Healing*. Church Information Board, London 1958.

36 Richards J. *The Church's Ministry of Healing* (an abridged version of the 1958 Report of the Archbishops' Commission). Marshall-Pickering, London 1986.

37 Anglican Consultative Council. *The Truth Shall Make You Free: The Lambeth Conference 1988*. Church House Publishing, London 1988, p 48-49.

38 Christian Medical Commission. *Healing and Wholeness: the Churches' Role in Health*. World Council of Churches, Geneva 1990.

6 THEOLOGY OF CREATION

The Church's ministry of healing does not take place on neutral territory. It is related to its context. Its purpose is at one with the purpose of its environment, God's creation. Hence the need to expound a theology of creation.

God the Creator

Belief in God as Creator is fundamental to the Christian Faith. The first article of the Apostles' Creed is:

> "I believe in God the Father Almighty,
> Creator of heaven and earth."

The Bible begins with the words, "In the beginning God created." The narrative declares that "God saw all that he had made, and it was very good" (Gen.1.31). This is taken to mean that God's purpose for every part of his creation is good. Though, as the story of the Fall makes plain, the creation is flawed (Gen.3).

This does not mean that God's universe is out of control; that some other power, responsible for evil, challenges God's sovereignty and threatens his good purpose. Christianity is not a dualistic religion. God takes responsibility for evil (Amos 3.6; Isa.45.7; Lam.3.38; Mic.1.12). God planted the tree of the knowledge of good and evil in the Garden of Eden (Gen.2.9), and Satan, called the shadow of God by Jung, was a member of God's household (Job 1.6). It is in the end more true and more satisfying to place the mystery of the origin of evil with God, and not elsewhere.

This insistence on the sovereignty of God helps us to face the problem of human misery. This is powerfully expounded in Job's complaint to God (Job 3.1-26), in which Job perceives that suffering is central to the human condition. As one commentator put it:

> "Man has been arbitrarily cast into life by a God who equally arbitrarily causes suffering from which there is no escape".[1]

Coping with Evil

We perceive evil differently as a child, as an adolescent and as an adult. Our understanding changes as we grow towards Christian maturity. Not only individuals but whole societies may grow or regress in their understanding of evil.

The origin of evil is nowhere explained in the Bible, but the fact of evil is clearly acknowledged. The Bible is the story of people who were affected by evil and who sought various ways of coping with its effects. Laws and rituals, ethical codes and religious rites attempted to contain, modify, or redeem human afflictions which stemmed from the flaw in creation.

In the Old Testament we see the development of Israel from slavery in Egypt to an association of tribes in the wilderness. At this level of development goodness and purity are maintained by the **exteriorization** of evil. We put it at arm's length outside ourselves (the 'scapegoat', Lev.16.20-22). It is what we do which counts (right actions), while what we think and feel (motivation) is not so carefully considered. Law and order are important, and the pursuit of moral perfection. The model of salvation in a society like that is the Exodus of the Hebrews from Egypt, in which the people are rescued out of the external evil of slavery. In their morality good and evil are similarly polarized, so that holiness is seen as being achieved by **separation** from evil.

As time went on, perceptions changed and the prophets proclaimed deeper and more disconcerting insights. They warned against reliance on cultic religious observances (sacrifices, fastings etc.) rather than on a true inner morality:

"To obey is better than sacrifice, and to listen to [God] better than the fat of rams." (1 Sam.15.22)

"For I require loyalty, not sacrifice, acknowledgement of God rather than whole-offerings." (Hos.6.6)

But the prophets also reach out to an understanding of the true springs of human morality:

"I shall set my law within them, writing it on their hearts." (Jer.31.33)

"Rend your hearts and not your garments." (Joel 2.13)

However, it does seem that the basic understanding of behaviour among the Jewish people remained more or less unchanged, and concentrated chiefly on external actions.

In the New Testament Jesus brings a new awareness into the old situation. In the Sermon on the Mount he expounds the importance of motivation in matters of morality. He who hates his brother is already on the way to murder (Matt.5.21-24). Jesus also points to the 'evil within' when he shows that a person is not defiled by eating with unwashed hands:

"Wicked thoughts, murder, adultery, fornication, theft, perjury, slander - these all proceed from the heart; these are the things that defile a person." (Matt.15.19-20)

It is the Cross of Jesus which is the new model of salvation; not a rescue like the Exodus, but a death which plumbs the depths of suffering. Not rescue from an evil situation but salvation in and through evil; confronting it, bearing it and transforming it.

But this transformation takes time, and in the New Testament both the old and new perceptions of evil exist side by side. Although the sheep and goats go their separate ways (Matt.25.31-46), Jesus asks forgiveness for those who crucify him. His new covenant does not separate evildoers and condemn them. Although Jesus exorcizes evil spirits, he also counsels "Do not resist those who wrong you" (Matt. 5.39). Christians no longer see their choices simply in relation to the great absolutes of good and evil but, knowing themselves imperfect, look in a different direction. Holiness is by **association** with a God who forgives and who transforms personal shadow and social evil through suffering.[2]

Reconciliation

The Spirit of God, always active in creation, found fullest expression and embodiment in Christ, whose ministry and death dealt radically with the powers of evil, and left the legacy of the Spirit for his Church to continue that ministry.

The New Testament describes this ministry in terms of reconciliation (2 Cor.5.18-21). Just as God was in Christ reconciling the world to himself, so Christ is in his Church:

- reconciling conflicting elements
- joining what evil has put asunder
- mending what is broken
- transforming evil through bearing it and suffering.

His Church is the vehicle of grace and the contemporary agent of the activity of the Spirit who brings hope and imparts the power whereby the wounds of humanity may be healed. Thus, the Spirit lifts humanity to its divine destiny, encouraging people to seek the means of grace which include:

- the Bible
- the sacraments
- good works
- the corporate life in the body of Christ.[3]

The Church's healing ministry is part of this ministry of reconciliation. If it is to be on the right lines, it must reflect and be derived from God's creative and redemptive activity. This means that the Church in its healing ministry must relate to the sick in ways which are compatible with those in which God relates to his creation. We look then at:

- the relationship of God to his creation
- the ways in which this relationship is characterized in the ministry of Jesus
- the relationship of human beings to God's creation.

God's Relationship to Creation

The Christian doctrine of creation is not primarily concerned with a theory of when and how the world began. It rather expresses a total attitude to the environment arising from the belief that it is dependable and trustworthy; an environment in which human beings enjoy freedom and exercise responsibility.

A craftsman who makes something, fashions it from materials which lie to hand. But God creates out of nothing. He "gives existence as well as essence".[4] Furthermore, God's creative activity implies a much more intimate relationship with his creation than is usually understood in the relationship between, say, a joiner and a piece of furniture which he makes. To say of a craftsman or artist that he 'puts himself into his work' hints at a profound truth which lies at the heart of the Christian doctrine of creation.[5] God is 'in' his creation. He is intimately related to it. His very life is in it. He breathes into human nostrils the breath of life (Gen.2.7). The living world owes its continuing existence to the creative Spirit of God who ceaselessly supplies and sustains its life.

The model of God with the highest profile in the Old Testament is that of the sovereign Lord who orders events by divine fiat. This is understandable since the Hebrews came to their monotheistic belief through hard experience. The country of their captivity (Babylon in the sixth century BC), initially the foreign land where their native songs could not be sung (Psa.137.4), came to be seen as the territory of the Lord. If there is no place where his rule does not hold sway, and no circumstances in which he is unable to come to his people's aid, then the Lord of history must be the King of creation; and he who "gathers in the scattered Israelites" (Psa.147.2) and "heals the broken in spirit" (Psa.147.3), is the one who "numbers the stars one by one and calls each by name" (Psa.147.4). Spatial metaphors are inevitable in our language about God. 'Height' and 'depth', 'beyond' and 'near', 'above' and 'within', are mutually exclusive if taken literally. Used to describe God's unique relationship to the world, however, they give expression to a continuing tension in our understanding of that relationship.

A biblically valid doctrine of creation must always reflect this tension. On the one hand, God cannot be part of creation in the sense of being one more object on which or person on whom I may exercise my faculties. One cannot by searching attain to the limits of God. His ways are past tracing out (Job 11.7; Psa.145.3; Rom.11.33). He is the infinite, detached, unapproachable, unknowable God. On the other hand, he is nearer than hands and feet, closer than breathing: "In him we live and move, in him we exist" (Acts 17.28). God is the

power behind every thought of my brain, every beat of my
heart, every breath of my body:

> "Centre and soul of every sphere,
> Yet to each loving heart how near."[6]

Throughout Christian history there have been recurring
attempts to separate the God of creation from the God of
redemption. But the continuing, main-stream tradition has
always insisted that there must be no such divorce.

The Ministry of Jesus

"The word became flesh" (John 1.14) identifies the Carpenter
of Nazareth as the Architect of the universe:

> "Through him all things came to be; without him no
> created thing came into being." (John 1.3)

Paul expounds a similar doctrine:

> "In him everything in heaven and on earth was created...
> the whole universe has been created through him and
> for him. He exists before all things, and all things are
> held together in him." (Col.1.16-17)

Yet the noble phrases "Jesus Christ is Lord" (Phil.2.11) and
"that at the name of Jesus every knee should bow - in heaven,
on earth and in the depths" (Phil.2.10) are part of a passage
encouraging the Christians at Philippi to be humble like
Jesus.

Our Lord's understanding of his own ministry lives with this
tension. He is the 'servant king'. He is the 'Lord's anointed',
coming not only to proclaim the Good News of the Kingdom
by word of mouth, but to announce that it was present in his
own person and work (Luke 11.20). The signs were manifest
to those with eyes to see. When John the Baptist from prison

sent messengers to ask if he were the expected Messiah, Jesus responded:

"Go and report to John what you hear and see: the blind recover their sight, the lame walk, lepers are made clean, the deaf hear, the dead are raised to life, the poor are brought the good news." (Matt.11.4-5)

The implication is obvious. Prophetic promises are being fulfilled (e.g. Isa.35.5-10). Signs of the kingdom of God abound. Messiah is here.

The crowds were impressed by the fact that Jesus met the varying circumstances of his ministry with authority. Mark draws attention to this in the early stages of his Gospel. People were amazed because, both in his teaching and in his handling of human disease, he displayed 'authority' (Mark 1.22 & 27). He felt no need to quote others (established and recognized authorities) in order to substantiate his statements, nor to use other names to dispel the fears of the demon-possessed. "I tell you" was sufficient to establish truth (e.g. Matt.5.20, 22, 28, 34, 39, 44), and "Stand up, take your bed, and walk" (Mark 2.9) was enough to restore the paralytic's strength and mobility without involving any other validating authority.

Yet this authority cannot be placed in the same category as the authoritarianism which characterizes the world's recognized rulers who "lord it over their subjects" (Mark 10.42). Jesus made this clear to his disciples when, on his last journey to Jerusalem, James and John asked for special status in the kingdom when Jesus came "in [his] glory" (Mark 10.37). The power and might popularly understood by the word 'glory' were worlds away from our Lord's understanding of the term. As the fourth Evangelist makes plain, the glorification of the Son of Man is inseparable from his humiliation (John 13.31); and Mark's account of our

Lord's response to the request of James and John unmistakeably sees the ministry of Jesus as the fulfilment of the great servant song in Isaiah (52.13-53.12). The Messiah's authority derives from his willingness to serve, and the kingly rule of God is most authentically demonstrated in the suffering servant who:

"was pierced for our transgressions,
crushed for our iniquities ...
and by his wounds we are healed." (Isa.53.5)

At Caesarea Philippi (Mark 8.27-33), Peter and doubtless the other disciples found this unbelievable and unacceptable. A suffering Messiah! Peter, scandalized at the thought,"took hold of [Jesus] and began to rebuke him" (Mark 8.32). But he had to learn the truth that the way of the Cross was the only route to the world's salvation. The Gospels reflect this inescapable tension between the authority of Jesus and his acceptance of a servant's menial role.

We see then, in our Lord's ministry, a reflection of the tension demonstrated in the two-sided relationship of God to his creation. The New Testament Evangelists testify, on the one hand, to the involvement of Jesus in the vulnerability of humanity, touched by our infirmities; hungry, thirsty, tired, angry and finally crucified. On the other hand, he is the authoritative healer, decisively defeating the forces of evil.

The Relationship of Human Beings to Creation

Human beings are both products of creation and participators in it. They are involved in God's continuing creation, co-workers together with him (1 Cor.3.9; 2 Cor.6.1). Since God is love (1 John 4.8), and Christian doctrine holds that the creative activity of God is the expression of his love, it follows that God not only affects his creation, but is affected by it. To love someone makes the lover vulnerable. His love

73

may be spurned, ignored or taken advantage of. The recipient of that love may use the status conferred by being loved as a vantage point from which to challenge or repudiate the lover's overtures.

When God exercises his creative love, he limits his power. The recipients of his love may spoil his work, harm his creation, and use its resources for selfish ends. The belief that the disease and disorder of the universe are one with the fall of creation has persisted in Christian thought. The relationship of the creator to humanity 'bruised and broken by the fall'[7], finds fullest expression in Jesus who was both 'victor and victim'[8] in the conflict with evil, and is the wounded healer.

When human beings engage in a ministry inspired by love, they too are vulnerable. Vanstone's exposition of his parable, derived from the activity of two boys in building a model of a tract of countryside, makes this plain. They "put themselves into it".[5] They are no longer detached observers, unaffected by the shape which their creation is assuming. The shape which it assumes could not evolve without their creative enterprise. Yet, as it evolves, it takes on a certain independent existence, challenging their right to determine what the next step shall be, questioning their decisions and affecting their own appraisal of what is happening. And all the time, they are being 'drawn into' their creation, affecting it, but also being affected by it.

This mutuality is, we believe, characteristic of all genuine Christian ministry. The relationship of people to God's creation reflects that of God's relationship to his creation, and that of the relationship of Christ to the world which he came to save. Hence those engaged in the Church's healing ministry need to be sensitive to both the opportunities and limitations of their calling. They will be aware that the importance of what they are engaged in may be measured:

- not primarily by its results in human well-being, but by its being a work of love
- not by the achievements wrought by their self-sufficient competence, but by their being open and vulnerable to what their commitment to ministry does to them
- not merely by their ability to affect the recipients of their service, but by their capacity to be affected by them and to recognize the mutuality of their relationship.

References

1   Cox D. *Man's Anger and God's Silence: The Book of Job*. St Paul Publications, Slough 1990.

2   Sanford JA. *Evil: the Shadow Side of Reality*. Crossroad, New York 1989.

3   Lambourne RA. The Cup of Cold Water and The Cup of Blessing. *Theology* 1961; 64: 495 ff.

4   Macquarrie J. *The Faith of the People of God*. SCM Press, London 1972, p 47.

5   Vanstone WH. *Love's Endeavour, Love's Expense*. Darton, Longman & Todd, London 1977.

6   Holmes OW (1809-94). 'Lord of all being, throned afar'. In: *The Methodist Hymnbook* (34th Edition). Methodist Conference Office, London 1962, no.32.

7   Hart J(1712 - 68). 'Come, ye sinners, poor and wretched'. In: *The Methodist Hymnbook* (34th Edition). Methodist Conference Office, London 1962, no.324.

8   Whale JS. *Victor and Victim*. Oxford University Press, Oxford 1960.

7   THE THEOLOGY OF HEALING

"What you call restoration to health
is only incubation of another malady."[1]

That the meaning of health is less obvious and much richer than at first appears can be illustrated with reference to the word *shalom*, used often in the Hebrew scriptures. *Shalom* encompasses various strands in the notion of health, conveying a sense of well-being and completeness in every dimension of life - physical, psychological, social and spiritual. It is experienced as gift and it looks to a fulfilment which can be found only in God. It is not only or even primarily the absence of disease. *Shalom* is a positive state of 'right-relatedness' to and of dependence on God. It is irreducibly corporate:

> "*Shalom* is not something that can be objectified and set apart. It is not the plus which the 'haves' can distribute to the 'have-nots', nor is it an internal condition (peace of mind) that can be enjoyed in isolation. *Shalom* is a social happening, an event in inter-personal relations. It can therefore never be reduced to a simple formula: it has to be found and worked out in actual situations."[2]

Comparable images in the New Testament are 'the Kingdom of God' (Mark and Luke), 'the Kingdom of heaven' (Matthew) and 'life', meaning new life in Christ (John). They all suggest a dynamic harmony and fulfilment which is indivisibly personal and corporate. Some aspects of these images will be touched on in more detail later in this chapter. In the meantime some general observations are in order.

From a Christian point of view we enjoy health when we are moving towards what God is preparing for us to enjoy and when we are collaborating with God in that preparation:

> "Health is thus a value and a vision word which has both to be brought constantly down to earth and to be related persistently to a promise, an aim and a hope which lies ahead and above us."[3]

Words like 'healthy' and 'healing' are always limited by their contexts. For example, healing may refer to the mending of a physical wound or of a relationship. Something is healthy if it is functioning as intended. A healing is the removal of an obstacle to health. In practice, perfect health is never achieved; it is always to be sought in ever-widening circles. From a Christian perspective, health is best thought of as an 'eschatological' idea:

> "It is what God promises and offers in the end...is available now both in foretastes and as the aim and ideal which... provokes us to more healthy responses and excites us to a search which is at the same time a seeking of health and an enjoying of health".[3]

In this sense, healing can be seen as the turning to good of the malfunctioning of creation, whether physical, psychological, social or environmental. It stands out in contrast to the fatalistic acceptance of a life of drastically diminished expectations. This last is the fruit of that voice in us which insists that things can never be significantly different from the way they are. This voice persuades people to be defined by their pains, limitations and disabilities rather than by the transfiguring word of promise.

What matters most is a person's self-image and self-identification. A change in these may or may not result in shifting the disease or mitigating the disability; but that is not the decisive point. The destiny of humanity is to know ourselves loved without limit or condition by God (1 Cor.13.12).

From a scientific point of view, the wonder of the world in general and of the human organism in all its particular complexity is that they function so well. Yet malfunctions occur and, at least in the case of humans, these are the focus of pain and sometimes of profound perplexity and suffering. The pain raises a question as to what can be done about it, while the perplexity is about the meaning of the malfunction: if I have to endure this sickness or disability what is the purpose of it? One view sees sickness as a result of the Fall (Gen.3). Another view sees it as the result of the processes of creation proceeding by trial and error (see opposite).

The fact remains, however, that it is hardly helpful for the sufferer to be told that what causes his pain is either a long-distant historic Fall or errors in creation, and as such part of the price we collectively pay for the kind of creation it is.

Yet the gift happens; people are unfrozen from anti-life postures. Sometimes very ill people or those with very severe disabilities become radiant. Out of persistent pain and profound anguish of spirit a new coinage is minted, and is an incomparable witness to the transcendent God who is closer to us than we are to ourselves. Thus, if we have eyes to see, creation's errors produce new possibilities of becoming fully human. But to see this we have first to be reduced to nothing. That is the way of it, the mystery and the wonder of it, beyond all calculation or planning. The gift requires only 'Yes'. It is sometimes those who are most ill (in terms of unawakened humanity, the weakest and of least account) who are most

"In a universe which offers vast possibilities of choice, evolution by random variation and natural selection ensures that a wide variety of the possible modes of being should be explored... The profusion of life, the immense variety, the mistakes, the dead-ends and the failures all make sense on this view of things. Free creativeness drawing on an inexhaustible well of randomness is bound to lead to tragedy and waste and suffering. But it also seems to be the only possible basis for those higher levels of freedom in terms of which Christians have always defended God's wisdom in creation. The alternative, a universe planned in detail and unfolding inexorably as pre-ordained, containing no source of unpredictability within itself, would not only be intolerably dull but also unforgivably evil. Why should whole species be created only to be exterminated? Why should the apparent design of some parts of many organisms be so remarkably inefficient? Why death, unless its counterpart reproduction were essential as a generator of newness?"[5]

obviously transparent to the divine presence. Healing has to do with becoming fully persons in a community of persons. Thus, it may make sense in some situations to speak of 'a severe mercy'.[4]

Questions might be asked as to whether or in what sense this 'Yes' has to do with faith, or about how divine initiative and human response work together. Since faith itself is a gift, the distinction between gift and response cannot be tidily sustained. There comes a point when the question of 'how' seems blasphemous in the face of the wonder of what is seen.

The New Testament nearly always reserves the word *sozo* (healing/salvation) for the direct speech of Jesus. Thus, Jesus says to the Samaritan with leprosy, "Your faith has [saved/healed] you" (Luke 17.19). Proclaiming the kingdom of God and healing are close companions in the gospel narratives. In addition, the New Testament stresses the corporate dimension of healing activity (Jas.5.14-16).

Healing is understood as a new relationship with God, manifested through relationships with other people and the environment. Similarly, because of the new relationships, healing can lead to cure. We can therefore say, "All can be healed, though not all are cured". There is also evidence in the gospel story of cure without healing (Matt.11.20-24), instances when Jesus did not find the response of praise and repentance for which he longed.

The claim already advanced that shifting the disease is not decisive has to take into account Jesus' works of healing, and the common assumption that healing is in itself the point. Two movements must be attended to, and they are at first glance mutually incompatible. The more obvious one is towards the alleviation of distress: feeding, exorcising, healing, raising from the dead. The other movement, also discernible from the beginning, is the one towards his death. There is a tendency, particularly when healing is the topic, to talk as if the first movement is the definitive one. This is strange, for there is no suggestion in the gospel narratives that those to whom Jesus ministered did not subsequently weaken and die. Again, the gospel narratives make clear that Jesus was not always available for healing purposes. He withdrew, sometimes in the face of pressing expectations (Mark 1.35-38). Most important, emphasis on Jesus' movement towards others' suffering as decisive takes no serious account of the drive towards his death. If the two movements are not considered together the story is spineless, with Jesus as just another healer who puzzlingly had to die.

The integrating insight here is that Jesus' movement towards death is the conscious entry into his own ultimate poverty, the lived acknowledgement that he is and has nothing of his own. This is that chosen victimhood which the New Testament proclaims as the saving of the world, in the sense that it changes the possibilities for the adventure of becoming human, just as Roger Bannister, the first man to run a mile in under four minutes, changed the possibilities for athletics. Jesus' healing works are signs of this death as the way in to newness of life. Two reactions to those signs are condemned in the gospels; denial of the sign, which is blasphemy; and stopping short at the sign, which is unbelief.[6]

Also noteworthy is the connection between Jesus' works of healing and forgiveness of sin. The healing of the paralytic (Mark 2.1-12) is not just about curing sickness but about forgiveness of sin and raising up into new life, as is the passage from the Letter of James (Jas.5.13-18). In our eagerness to deny that sickness is **punishment** for sin ("It was not that he or his parents sinned... he was born blind so that God's power might be displayed in curing him" John 9.3) we may miss a crucial point. If forgiveness of sin is understood as the setting free of the desire for God, sin is not the denial of that desire but whatever gives it an inadequate or mistaken focus. Given that this desire is fundamental to being human, it is to be expected that anything which thwarts it will make us ill. It is not that God wishes to punish us but that failure to take seriously our restlessness short of God puts us at odds with our true selves. Remember the young man in the gospel who could not follow Jesus because he was tied to his great wealth (Mark 10.22).

This is not grounds for blame or recrimination, but rather for a compassion which recognizes the predicament as universal. Sin is primarily a condition in which the entire human race finds itself, as both victim and perpetrator, impeding growth into our true identity in God. The condition is age-old and world-wide, so there can be no easy equation between the particular sins of an individual and the specific dis-ease he manifests. It is rather a question of things unresolved between individuals or groups in one generation pursuing a life of their own into the next, with dire consequences:

"Parents eat sour grapes, and their children's teeth are set on edge." (Eze.18.2)

It is this dynamic which Jesus' death puts into reverse.

The liberation of our deepest desire to find its proper focus in the divine mystery is the healing of humanity. Traditional images such as 'the healing of the nations' and 'a new heaven and a new earth' suggest the appropriate scale here. Any apparent healing which is not a point of entry into new life is at best ambiguous. The healing with which we are concerned either has cosmic bearings or is nothing very much. It brings the universe alive and ourselves within it as beloved of God. It ends the divorce which declares two worlds, one of the dead and the other of the living. This split which threatens us with the world of the dead is ended in the resurrection of

Jesus, which means that we and those who have died are one radiant company, the communion of saints. The barriers are down, and healing can proceed.

The coming of the risen Jesus to his own, bearing his wounds, means that he who was their wounding becomes their healing, in accord with the axiom that 'what wounds heals'. This is not to say that everything which wounds brings healing (this is patently not the case) but that if there is to be healing it must come by way of what wounds. If Jesus becomes the wounded healer he is in the first instance the disciples' wounding. How can this be? A recently suggested answer is that they had an addictively dependent relationship with him before the crucifixion.[7] This immature dependence on him is the wounding of them, for it involves a distorted expectation which can only lead to a uniquely dreadful disillusionment.[8]

What is addiction? It is the derailment of the desire for the infinite (i.e. God) by attachment instead to a finite object. The mistake is to suppose that we must subdue the desire which the addiction evokes, for that would be to deny the wonderful secret at the heart of all addiction. True healing involves letting go of the finite object which, taken as without limit, has been running us. Then and only then can the desire find its proper focus in the divine mystery, shown forth to the desolate disciples in and through the risen Lord, Jesus the Christ.

So much that passes for healing, not least among Christians, is in grave danger of not taking account of the desire for the infinite. The situation of a drug addict to whom all that has happened is the withdrawal from drugs is extremely dangerous: an addictive tendency lacking a focus. Anyone who aspires to the explicitly Christian dimension of healing would do well to remember Jesus' image of the house swept clean and tidy (Matt.12.43-45).

It is important to beware of any picture of healing as merely the restoration to function in a society which, from the gospel's point of view, is still committed to death. In such a society we have to take seriously the necessarily de-stabilizing aspect of a gospel which proclaims a healing death as the world's salvation. Once the thirst for God is aroused, however addictive the form of its activation, there is no going back to what we were about, which is mostly what other people want us to do so that their world may be kept in place. The essence of sin is "other people telling me who I am and I believing them". Collusion with inauthentic images of myself can only be a denial of the irreducible originality of the given self, and thus an offence to God.[9] In this sense sin is closely linked to a great deal of ill-health; for to believe and to enact a lie about myself, however unconsciously or for whatever noble motives, can only be conducive to sickness.

We cannot experience what wholeness is, because we have not yet fully found it. Such experience is for the future, and corporate. Our nature as human is to be so bound up one with another that it makes no sense to talk about my well-being in isolation from that of everybody else. The characteristic work of the living God is the forming of a people for himself.

In any case we are on the inside of the story of humanity, a story certainly unfinished and perhaps only in its beginnings. So much is necessarily tentative and exploratory. Our world offers a vast range of therapies, and while some can be controlling and intrinsically addictive, the lack of a Christian label is not in itself a basis for suspicion. It must also be recognized that **anything** can become addictive, from the National Health Service to the sacraments. Likewise, any therapeutic approach - whether charismatic healing, psychotherapy, or hospice care - can be used manipulatively by its practitioners to acquire or retain power over others. Pastoral studies rightly emphasize enabling, but such an image of the carer's task can be just as controlling as more authoritarian approaches. Am I really being enabled to become my true self, or merely to act out the would-be enabler's projection of the person I ought to be?

In essence, Christian faith is not problem-solving but mystery-encountering, so that any particular sickness is part of a much wider and deeper picture. A common mistake is to suppose that the Christian approach to healing is problem-solving, the illness or disability being the problem. This puts something called Christian healing in the market-place along with all the other competing therapies which seem largely unaware of or intolerant of one another's claims.

Even a serious illness such as cancer acquires a distorted significance when it is made the centre of the picture. A problem-centred approach assumes that there is a solution, but Christian faith invites us further and further into the mystery.[10] The fact that someone for whose cure we pray is not cured recalls us to the sovereignty of God in every particular of human life, and calls forth a deeper trust, often dearly bought, that the gift is in the ordeal. Our identity is being forged in the crucible of whatever sufferings turn out to be inextricable from the particular journey of each person, and of us together, into fullness of life.

Healing is never just cure. What else it is may be either good (e.g. a sign of new life) or bad (e.g. return to function in an unchanged situation). Some people would argue for a third category, indifferent; but that is to forget that there is no neutrality within the dynamic of salvation. We are always either being saved or perishing, whether cured or not. That is the knife-edge on which we live.

References

1   Eliot TS. *The Family Reunion*. Faber and Faber, London 1960, p 66.
2   Davies JG. *Worship and Mission*. SCM Press, London 1966, p 130.
3   Jenkins D. In: McGilvray J (ed). *The Quest for Health and Wholeness*. German Institute for Medical Missions, Tubingen 1981, p xii-xiii.
4   Vanauken S. *A Severe Mercy*. Hodder & Stoughton, London 1977.
5   Habgood J. *A Working Faith*. Darton, Longman and Todd, London 1980, p 15.
6   Hoskyns EC & Davey N. *Crucifixion - Resurrection*. SPCK, London 1981, chapter 8.
7   Moore S. *The Paschel Mystery: Source of Liberating Grace*. Unpublished paper 1990.
8   Harvey NP. *Death's Gift*. Epworth Press, London 1985.
9   Harvey NP. *The Morals of Jesus*. Darton, Longman and Todd, London 1990, chapters 11 & 12.
10 Taylor J. On not solving the problem. *CMS Newsletter* 1971; no. 353.

8   CARE OF THE UNCURED

"I am unwell but there is no treatment available; I face the possibility of death but I am not dying at the moment. I ask myself 'Where can I go for help?' and feel angered that the response is 'nowhere'. The Medical Director of a hospice could neither answer my question nor offer to help, because I do not fit into one of their categories. It seems the criterion for hospital admission is that the patient must benefit from medical treatment; the need to be cared for is not enough. Outpatient review for the uncured is infrequent - no point bringing us back if there is nothing to be done. This all adds to my sense of rejection and confirms our suspicions that we the uncured are of little value. We even fail to make the doctor feel good because we cannot make use of his medical or surgical skills."[1]

The above was penned by a 33 year-old curate with an inoperable tumour of the brain-stem. Continuing disability is a reality of life for her and many others.

Those ministering to people who specifically seek the Church's ministry of healing see many who return again and again to the altar rail of their church or the consultation room at a Christian healing centre. These people continue to carry the marks of an outward disability or the inner burden of destructive emotions. Some seem to receive only the strength and desire to keep going, while others appear to move on and grow into new areas of fruitfulness, despite the handicap.

The uncured, and those who assist them, face particular difficulties which can easily be neglected when looking at the interface of hospice and healing, of death and cure. While the goals in hospice care are not seen purely in terms of physical comfort, death is on the near horizon. Caring for the uncured has no such drama and no such horizon. In addition, the challenges presented by the person with, for example, Alzheimer's disease ('senile dementia') differ markedly from those surrounding a child born with brain damage or a malfunctioning heart. This chapter, while having a wider relevance, is focused on physical limitation (e.g. spina bifida, paraplegia, cystic fibrosis).

Responses to Loss

Commonly, a series of losses has to be coped with. These may include the loss of:

- normal family life
- sexual expression
- career and status
- motivation
- independence
- mobility and use of the senses
- continence.

Responses to these losses often follow a recognizable pattern, beginning with shock and progressing erratically through denial, questioning, anger, guilt, grief and anxiety to a state of acceptance or resignation. These responses are similar to those seen in people facing death.[2,3] Generally, movement is not linear and people may well move backwards as well as forwards in the process of adjustment. Some components of the journey may be short, or even non-existent. Others are lengthy and may become sticking points (Figure 1). The pattern of responses varies not only from person to person

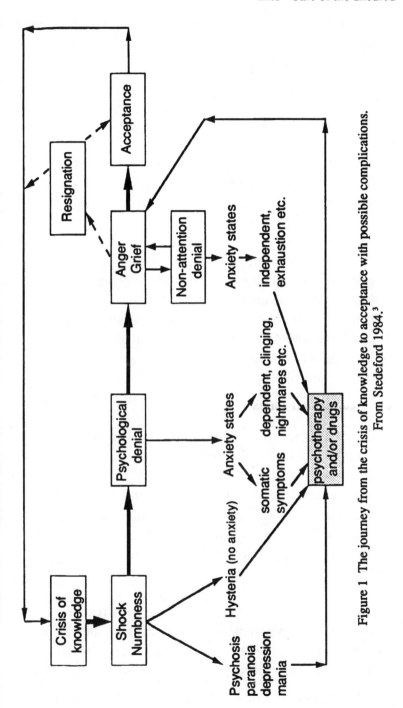

Figure 1   The journey from the crisis of knowledge to acceptance with possible complications. From Stedeford 1984.[3]

but also in the same person when grieving for different losses. The process can be thought of as movement from:[1]

$$\left.\begin{array}{l}\text{disorientation}\\\text{disorganization}\\\text{disintegration}\end{array}\right\}\ \text{to}\ \left\{\begin{array}{l}\text{re-orientation}\\\text{re-organization}\\\text{re-integration}\end{array}\right.$$

| ('crucifixion') | ('resurrection') |

Because emotions are ever-present, the process of adjustment goes on at varying levels 24 hours a day. At times this will be very exhausting. It is a process which has to be 'gone through' rather than 'got over'.

"You discover an area of loss and grieve for it. Part of grieving seems to be that you discover other areas of loss beyond the original. First, I grieved because I could not have children. Then I had to face the effect of this on potential relationships; I felt unable to marry. This led me to question my sexuality, my creativity and my contribution to ongoing creation; to look at the very purpose of my life. The whole struggle is like climbing a hill. You think the summit is in sight but then you discover what you thought was the top is actually just part of the journey."[1]

Shock causes emotional numbness, and is particularly marked when the consequences and implications of a diagnosis are imparted without warning. This 'anaesthetizing' of the mind is helpful in that it allows the person to assimilate the bad news gradually.

Denial allows what cannot be endured to be ignored. Life is lived as if in a dream because reality is hell, and the face smiles as if to prove that nothing is wrong. Denial is a necessary defence or coping mechanism which we all constantly use, albeit in different ways:[4]

- **existential denial** is the capacity to believe that one's mortality is not threatened by impending danger in everyday life
- **psychological denial** is defence against the anxiety which flows from impending danger. For example, someone may repeatedly 'forget' what he has been told about diagnosis and prognosis
- **non-attention denial** is when someone accepts the diagnosis and prognosis, makes plans accordingly, and then lives day to day as if nothing is wrong.

Psychological denial is usually eroded in time by the inescapable consequences of disability. One teenager with sickle cell anaemia wrote:

> "I remember when I used to think that this was just a passing phase I was going through and that things could only get better. How wrong I was."[5]

Questioning begins the search for meaning and purpose despite disability. In his frustration, Job cried out to God:

> "Why was I not stillborn,
> Why did I not perish when I came from the womb?
> Why is life given to those who find it so bitter?"
> (Job 3.11,20)

A diving accident which left a young woman paralysed from the neck down when aged 17 caused desolation, depression, and a wish to die. Out of her physical immobility and mental confusion, she repeatedly cried, "Why did you let this happen, God?" It was years before she was able to let go of the questioning, but eventually she wrote: "Only God knows **why** I was paralysed...but now I really am happy".[6]

Anger is an expression of frustration and of protest. It can also be a plea for restoration of what has been lost. Anger needs a target:

- the (awful) food
- the nursing care
- the doctor
- friends who visit
- God.

The teenager with sickle cell anaemia focused his anger on his friends:

> "During a painful episode when I am bedridden and can't move a muscle, my *alter ego* seems to appear. I find myself incredibly angry and almost vengeful. I despise my friends because they have never had to go through half of this and never will. Their lives seem so free of problems and yet I hear them talk about the pressure of school."[5]

However, when an uncured person feels defenceless and abandoned, anger may lead to a determination to survive.

> "Anger is at its greatest when it is a cry for love, and the person who suffers silently, stoically, has usually settled for hopelessness."[7]

Guilt may be an expression of inverted anger, targeted at oneself in the form of self-blame. Appropriate ('true') feelings of guilt may grow from the realization that one's chosen behaviour or activity caused the illness. On the other hand, much guilt is inappropriate ('false') and relates to feelings or concern that:

- thoughts are sometimes suicidal
- absence of physical healing is a judgement from God
- one feels anger against God
- one no longer has any faith in God
- "If only I had... it would not have happened."

Grief   for the loss of what might have been takes over as anger is expressed and worked through. Grief brings a time of loneliness, depression and withdrawal which is dominated by a feeling of being unloved and unlovable. The latter is accentuated if the ability to achieve is lost. A feeling of being abandoned may in fact be reality as friends find themselves unable to cope with a prolonged grief reaction. Resentment of dependence on others may prolong grief, and increasing dependence may precipitate more grief. It may also lead to renewed thoughts of suicide or, in a progressive disorder, the desire that the end will come soon.

Tears may act as a catalyst on the journey to acceptance and should not be discouraged. Crying, as an expression of physical, psychological, or spiritual pain, is a natural, God-given function which often brings a sense of relief and relaxation.[8] Tears are beyond words and yet may also help in finding words. The ability to cry, however, is often affected by physical state, social environment and the expectation of others. Christians who naively believe that Christianity should be lived only with a smile will need permission to mourn and cry.

Anxiety   may accompany any of the above responses to loss. It is often coupled with anger or fear. Anxiety may relate to:

- separation from an 'attachment figure'
- difficulty in adjustment to a changed environment
- seeming loss of control, of either self or circumstances
- poor communication
- unresolved past experiences
- unmanageable pain
- having no say in treatment decisions
- a loss of privacy
- fear of an uncertain future.

Why Me?

"Grieve for the loss, the separation,
  Why me, why me?
Grieve for the loneliness, the rejection,
  Why me, Oh why me?
Feel the shock, the desperation,
  Why pick on me?
So stamp, so scream and shout, destruction,
  My fault, my guilt?

Feel the gloom and the depression,
  No talk, no talk!
The most unutterable oppression.
  Don't speak, won't speak!
Unspoken thoughts, so silent home. Home?
  Bursting, breaking
Help me Oh *carer* to mourn, to moan,
  And in mourning, peace!" '

Anxiety is hard to help until it is acknowledged and identified. This is a particular problem for those Christians who feel that anxiety is a denial of faith.

Acceptance

With time and appropriate support, a realization that despite permanent loss of health, life can still be lived may bring an acceptance which finds purpose in living. For example, Helen Keller grew to a place where she was able to say:

> "I thank God for my handicaps, for through them I have found myself, my work and my God."[10]

For some, however, resolution never comes, and there may merely be a sullen resignation which longs for death. Of those who achieve a state of positive acceptance, some see their suffering as being used intangibly in the transformation of the totality of human suffering (see chapter 2).

Many who find a transforming acceptance in the face of incurability, attempt to throw light and hope into a pool of pain and darkness. One mother, who had two severely handicapped children, has spoken of how she sees suffering as an incomparable reassurance of the existence and love of God.[11] Someone afflicted for more than 20 years with progressively disabling disease of the spine writes:

> "While on the more superficial level I fight both pain and dependence, deep down I find myself grateful for my situation which draws me ever deeper to the pierced heart of Christ, to whom I am consecrated and who continues to be reflected in the lives of the powerless, the suffering and the outcast."[12]

And the 33 year-old curate tells of how:

"I reached something of a crisis a couple of weeks ago but then made a great discovery. I had been fighting myself, not wanting to be seen as pathetic or to be wallowing in self pity, yet all the time feeling like I wanted to break. Then it seemed that my definition of breaking as disintegration was wrong, and what God was asking was that I surrender in my brokenness to his healing love. I came to see that letting go was not at all the same as giving up and that going with the situation was not to be confused with giving in to it... This all brought great peace and I give thanks for it." [1]

Acceptance of incurability can:

- open up new possibilities through new discoveries about oneself
- lead to a sense of liberation despite the limitations
- restore a sense of control
- transform the individual's sense of purpose
- restore self-esteem
- reduce feelings of isolation
- restore relationships
- ease physical pain
- impart to those who care the courage to go on
- enable one to participate in the reconciling work of Christ.

The challenge of care

In order to rise to the challenge of caring for the uncured, the carers have "to inspire a sense of worth, hope and purpose in existence".[13] In practice, they need:

- vision to believe that the losses which are evident provide potential for gain
- discernment to recognize the responses to loss that accompany incurable illness

- perseverance to press on with ordinary repetitive daily care
- courage to be a constant companion on a journey which stretches indefinitely into the future.

Care of the uncured is "an area between rehabilitation and terminal care which places the highest demands on the carer's skills"[14] (Table 1). Such care may well involve more 'being with' than 'doing to'.

The Needs of the Uncured

These are similar to those of the dying and embrace physical, psychological, social and spiritual dimensions. An accepting and dependable environment which is available to meet future needs allows truth to be faced without haste and without overdependency. The person needs to feel involved in treatment decisions, and not to be ignored or talked over (see chapter 10). Good communication forms, sustains and restores personal identity.

The uncured need opportunities for creative and meaningful living to minimize the frustration of limitation and the constant awareness of ill-health which erode optimism and hope. The practicality of this differs widely, and depends partly on the restrictions imposed by disability. For example, the way in which a person with paraplegia undertakes wood-carving or horticulture will differ from the way such activities would be tackled by someone with hemiplegia following a stroke.

Care lacks real meaning for the incurable as long as the carers remain strangers. There is a need for the walls of fear which separate them from the carers to be broken down so that there is a true meeting on the ground of our common humanity.[15]

Table 1   Responses to loss and challenges for the carers

Component	Challenge
Shock	To provide time and a dependable, accepting and enabling environment which allows truth to be faced by the person concerned without inappropriate dependency
Denial	To open new opportunities for purposeful and creative living that eventually diminish the need for denial
Anger	To accept and hear anger in the uncured; to enable the sufferer to pinpoint anger and to identify what is needed from the carers
Guilt	To discern true guilt and to facilitate repentance and forgiveness To bring love and understanding which impart the "courage to accept oneself as accepted in spite of feeling unacceptable",[16] not so much to give of one's riches but to reveal the other person's riches
Questioning	To avoid offering superficial answers or untruths that only feed the unanswerable 'why me?'
Grief	To acknowledge the appropriateness of grief and to 'weep with those who weep' without attempting to give answers To enter into solidarity with them and not walk away
Anxiety	To provide stability, reassurance and understanding To enable the individual to feel safe by planning continuing care for the days ahead To help in the rebuilding of self-esteem
Acceptance and resignation	To meet people where they are psychologically, and not to force them into an outward show of acceptance and the suppression of negative emotions in order to ease the carer's distress To recognize that acceptance can fluctuate with changing circumstances, and that denial and other responses to loss may periodically recur

The uncured may need protection from inappropriate evangelism and prayers for miraculous cure. Their spiritual needs are more often met through an offering of love and reconciliation, and an imparting of self-worth and purpose. Their needs are **not** met through a pastoral ministry which focuses on miracles; rather, on one which sees the presence of Jesus as the means for transforming lives through a realization that:

- nothing can separate us from the love of God
- love continues however slender is one's hold on life
- the most severe physical disability need not prevent one from both receiving and giving love.

This transformation may be manifested physically, psychologically, socially or spiritually. The uncured who are ready to receive will recognize God's power of love at work. Their needs will be met, however, only as they experience the care of a loving Father through the hands and hearts of their carers. This experience leads to healing in unexpected ways.

Occasionally something will happen to make spirits soar.

Disability deceased

Legs leaden, languishing lifeless in paralysis
Leap deftly, dancingly, waltzing with their Lord.
Eyes, blinded, discerning dull darkness
Drink in dazzling Christ-like light.
Ears, silenced, sensing no sound
Hear holy words of heaven's Host.
Mind, maimed, trapped yet tickled by simplest
   thought
Thrills joyously jubilant at Unending Love.[1]

More often people are enabled to live their everyday lives more fully despite ongoing limitations. For the uncured - as for the rest of us - lives are not lived on the mountain top (perhaps attempting to feed on signs and wonders) or on a race track with runners (running after a God found only in the supernatural) but in the day to day practicalities and limitations of living.

The Heart of Caring

At the heart of caring, love, hope, worth, and purpose have to be communicated and received through language, touch and actions. These have to be conveyed with poverty of heart and compassion.

'Poverty of heart' is that quality which enables the carer to see life as a gift to be shared rather than a property to be defended. The carer will find that the uncured are free to enter into a mutual solidarity once this poverty of heart is discerned. It brings a lack of preoccupation with a personal agenda, and so allows the uncured person to become an intimate friend. The carer will find that listening can take place without any attention to formulating answers; attention can be given without any concern about having to give.[15] Paradoxically, the carer may begin to feel a failure and become conscious of making mistakes. Yet, because of this, the same carer becomes an inspiration to the one cared for without knowing it.

The language of care is often unspoken; it includes humour, listening, confronting and prayer. **Humour** allows a sense of the ridiculous to lighten the load. Laughter can:

- strengthen bonds
- ease tensions
- make the unbearable seem bearable.

Rightly used, humour and laughter are both agents of healing. So too is **listening**, which is more than opening ears and closing lips:

> "You must go deeper and discover what it means to listen: to listen deeply to another, to the cry flowing from the heart, in order to understand people, both in their pain and in their gift." [17]

Listening is a form of loving attention which:

- gives value to the one who feels of no value
- imparts respect and sincerity
- allows an entering into the other's pain
- allows the mind space to untangle thoughts, concerns and relationships
- takes skill, time and commitment (see chapter 10).

Confronting   prevents the uncured from clinging to false expectations and hopes that are based on unreality. Gentle but firm confrontation can facilitate growth towards maturity and bring a deepening of relationship.

> "Carers often fear patients will become dependent on them and that this is unhealthy. I think it might be necessary. The newborn are dependent; they then search for independence and, if all goes well, become interdependent. I feel this pattern repeats when one's circumstances are newborn. As the Body of Christ should we not to some degree depend on each other just as we depend on Christ and on God? This dependence here is in the context of a relationship and would be better described as interdependence." [1]

Prayer   here is a spreading out of the carer's helplessness before God, with the knowledge of the enabling prayer support of the wider Church. It is in partnership with Christ that the carer seeks to bring a new dimension to participation in the sufferings of others. In this interdependence, prayers need not necessarily be said; caring in itself is the language of prayer.

Reflecting on his blindness, Milton wrote:

> "God doth not need
> Either man's work or His own gifts. Who best
> Bear His mild yoke, they serve Him best. His state
> Is Kingly. Thousands at His bidding speed,
> And post o'er land and ocean without rest:
> They also serve who only stand and wait." [18]

Touch speaks loudest when the nature of the infirmity, the physical changes of illness (emphasized by a glance in the mirror) and the loss of self-worth leave the uncured feeling untouchable. Touch, therefore: [19]

- restores love, security and a sense of being valued
- lifts isolation and conveys unquestioning acceptance
- facilitates a sharing of emotional feelings
- may cause the release and outpouring of pent-up emotions
- communicates where words fail to
- "meets dependency needs that may result from pain"
- expresses concern and compassion.

Carers need to consider in what circumstances touch and personal distance are therapeutically relevant. Touch may, for example, interrupt the natural expression of grief. For some, being touched may be abhorrent (see chapter 10).

> "All who tend the sick will bear in mind the maxim: To touch is not a technique; not touching is a technique." [20]

Actions express love and as such speak of relationship. In caring for the uncured, relationships matter more than results. There is no place for 'doing good' but always a place for 'sharing with'. Carers can provide opportunities for creativity by helping to draw out talents which have become submerged by the awfulness of disease and others which previously had not been recognized.

Action may just involve being or staying and not abandoning. It is not unusual to hear, "Whenever the doctor calls I feel better although I know there is nothing he can do." In such ways a sense of worth, hope and purpose in existence is achieved and maintained.

Compassion is the 'cement' which holds everything together. It draws carer and cared-for together in their common humanity.

> "Compassion asks us to go where it hurts, to enter into places of pain, to share in brokenness, fear, confusion and anguish. Compassion challenges us to cry out with those in misery, to mourn with those who are lonely, to weep with those in tears." [21]

With such compassion, the carer may not always need to ask the uncured about their feelings. This compassion is also necessary in relation to the 'hidden sufferers', that is, family and friends, who are so easily ignored and left to one side.

Care of the Uncured: Points to Remember

- Do not encourage the disabled to live in a dream because reality is hell. It is preferable to attempt to transform reality or give support to face the hell.
- Do not allow privacy to become separation and loneliness. These soon transform into guilt and self-

rejection, with feelings of worthlessness and abandonment. Space and privacy encourage respect; isolation and separation imply rejection.

- Be prepared to receive; the incurable have a gift for you which will enrich your life. When the incurable are perceived as teachers, then the help they are looking for can be safely offered.

- Beware of working in isolation. The needs of those being cared for can be overwhelming, leading to the escape of being 'unavailable' and the avoidance of the demanding patient (see chapter 12).

- Avoid being condescending. "Do not be surprised at rejection by broken people... They have suffered so much from broken promises, from people wanting to learn from experiments or to write a thesis and then... going away and never coming back. Rejected people are sick and tired of 'good' and 'generous' people, of people who claim to be Christians, of people who come to them on their pedestals of pride and power to do them good." [17]

Patronizing behaviour, with comments aside, affords the disabled person the status of a cabbage.

"Older people either stared or talked to the person pushing me. In one shop I handed my money to the cashier and she gave the change to my sister. 'Is she all right?', she asked, as I sat there, my brain perfectly in tune." [22]

"Hell is other people visiting", said a lady in a Cheshire Home. "I am patted on the back and told, 'There, there, you'll be all right'. I just want to hide when the do-gooders come round."

- Be aware that carers can easily collude together, seeing the 'good patient' as full of smiles and thanks who requests the minimum of attention; and the 'bad patient' as the one who is impatient, critical and demanding of attention.

- Do not collude with relatives whose own needs may bring pressure with comments such as, 'It's time you got over the shock of your illness now'. On the other hand, relatives may need help not to dilute the prognosis unrealistically for their own comfort.

- Do not encourage 'living in the past'. Emphasis on the joy of past events and achievements may promote feelings of guilt and serve to deny the reality of the present experience of failure. To encourage the belief that, 'I am who I was' equates identity with past productivity and success. This opens the door to bitterness.

- Avoid offering 'good advice' because this may create a barrier rather than facilitating involvement. The uncured need to find their own answers.

> "Advice may put people back together again but it cannot change them. Advice touches the surface of personality, not the centre. To give advice is to place oneself above one's fellow, thereby obstructing the spiritual fellowship in which he can be helped."[23]

Providing answers may stifle appropriate anger and grief. The fact that there are often no answers may result in anger with God. But carers who feel a need to defend God may simply be trying to cover up their own unacknowledged doubts and uncertainties.

'Chronic niceness' in the carer will tend to elicit comparable niceness in the uncured, with the result that negative feelings are not readily shared and resentments accumulate. When the carer's resources are finally exhausted, temper outbursts occur, with mixed results. While they release momentary tension, they strain the relationship.[24]

The 'personal agenda' of the carer may be a barrier to real concern. Likewise the 'need to be needed' may overrule and lead to an inappropriate model of caring. It is important to remember that both carer and cared-for are on a journey together, a journey deeper into God:

> "The 'uncured' person does not come into being at the moment of diagnosis. She has a personality and a history, both of which will affect the way in which she approaches her changed circumstances. These factors will consequently affect the outcomes the carers may expect from their care. If Joe was a cantankerous old so-and-so before his illness, he is quite likely to remain one afterwards. Carers must resist the temptation to expect the disabled to become virtuous angels but help them to retain their individuality. Healing is not intended to produce clones; we do not all become the same as we grow in wholeness. Rather we become more fully our wonderful individual selves, known, loved and accepted by God, just as we have been from the moment he watched us being formed in our mother's womb.

> Like all journeys, that of the uncured will have its joys and pains, its beauty and its ugliness, its riches and its poverty. There will be times of fun and times of frustration, times when you both wish the other was not there. It will be right to spend time together and time apart, to take time to find the strength to persevere. Through it all both carer and cared-for will discover that life can be lived until the very moment of death."[1]

In this way carer and cared-for can share the disabilities of our common humanity.

> "Weakness is our common suffering,
> Let frail courage be our meeting ground;
> For strength is not of our creation,
> But gentlest gift of Humble Truth."[1]

The Cost of Caring

> "Once we know that we are poor, the Kingdom of Heaven is ours. So when our lot is cast with somebody who is finding his Cross, his desert, his poverty overwhelming, we are on holy ground."[17]

In offering God's love to the uncured the carer may feel emotionally and spiritually drained, as well as open and vulnerable. The carer is faced with personal limitations and a sense of inadequacy in trying to discern the activity of God in the crushing defeats of everyday life. There are, however, occasions of immense joy. Not every experience is Gethsemane, although the carers often find themselves in a place of pain, wounded by the paradoxes and conflicts of life. Carers may physically express the pain they are carrying in recurrent ill-health. Carers, all too easily, stagger under heart-rending burdens in the busyness of the day and find exhaustion of mind and body hindering them, particularly initially. There is need to learn to leave the burdens of the day at the foot of the Cross, and to hold up the total situation to God in silent prayer. Carers are among the pain-bearers of society. They have to bear the cost of caring if they are to bear its fruit.

The conflicts of life have to be recognized as part of the Easter mystery, in that there is a necessity for death before resurrection. This is true for both the carers and the uncured.

Only by the experience of repeated small deaths in their own lives can carers know the meaning of resurrection. If the caring community is to be a sign of the Kingdom of God it must reveal a new kind of humanity. It is not just a collection of people, perhaps with a personal faith, who have been called to be alongside the sick and wounded. Rather, it is the relatedness of these individuals that is at the heart of caring and is the key to living the Gospel. In caring, the carers will also receive healing and a new self-understanding. Thus, it is in caring for another that a healing community is born.

References

1   Walker HM. Personal communication, 1991.
2   Kubler-Ross E. *On Death and Dying*. Macmillan, New York 1969.
3   Nighswonger C. Ministry to the dying as a learning encounter. *Journal of Thanatology* 1971; 1: 101-108.
4   Pattison E. *The Experience of Dying*. Prentice Hall, London 1977.
5   Daniels D. Sickle cell anaemia: a patient's tale. *British Medical Journal* 1990; 301: 673.
6   Eareckson J. *Joni*. Pickering & Inglis, London 1978, p 206.
7   Campbell A. *The Gospel of Anger*. SPCK, London 1986, p 95.
8   Van Heukelem J. Weep with those who weep. *Christian Counsellor's Journal* 1980; 1 (4): 2.
9   Crosher S. 'Why me?' In: *Good Grief*. Cruse, London 1987, p 41.
10 Keller H. Quoted in *Healing and Wholeness* 1991; 1: 40
11 Craig M. *Blessings* 1979. Quoted in: Longford F. *Suffering and Hope*. Collins Fount, London 1990, p 25.
12 Makower F. Faith or Folly? Darton, Longman & Todd, London 1989, p 112.
13 Jourard SM. *The Transparent Self*. Van Nostrand Reinhold, New York 1971.
14 Williams A. Incurable illness. *British Medical Journal* 1990; 301: 67.
15 Nouwen H. *Aging*. Doubleday, London 1974, p 106 & 144.
16 Tillich P. *The Courage to Be*. Fontana, London 1979.

17   Vanier J. *The Broken Body*.   Darton, Longman & Todd, London 1988.
18   Milton.   Sonnet 'On His Blindness' *English Poems of John Milton*. Oxford University Press, Oxford 1913.
19   Autton N. *Touch*. Darton, Longman & Todd, London 1989.
20   Older J. *Touching is Healing*. Stein and Day, New York 1982.
21   Nouwen H. *Compassion*. Darton, Longman & Todd, London 1982, p 4.
22   McCann R. My 'one in a million' chance. *British Medical Journal* 1990; **301**: 1483.
23   Tournier P. *Escape from Loneliness*. SCM Press, London 1962, p 159.
24   Augsburger DW. *Anger and Assertiveness in Pastoral Care*. Fortress Press, Philadelphia 1979.

SECTION III : CARE

---

9 PARTNERSHIP IN CARE: THE CHALLENGE OF TEAMWORK

"[Hospice] care is a matter of human relationships. There are skills to be learned and insights which can be gained from reading books, but the challenge and the reward of [hospice] care arises from the fact that it demands that we use the whole of ourselves to relate to our fellow human-beings who are in trouble. This can only be learned by experience in a community in which relationships are valued and fostered".[1]

Caring for dying people and their families is stressful.[2] It is commonly assumed that working in a team helps to diffuse the stress by spreading it among the various professional carers. Teamwork, however, may also create stress in that working with others is itself demanding.[3,4]

Authentic teamwork requires a group of people who:[5]
- possess individual expertise
- are responsible for making individual decisions
- hold a common purpose
- meet to communicate, share and consolidate knowledge
- establish agreed goals
- integrate care plans
- are committed to their own and each other's personal growth.

Teamwork implies coordination of effort. It facilitates the identification of available resources and avoids wasteful duplication. When discussing teamwork, it is necessary to consider individual members, shared purpose, group consciousness, and interdependence.

Individual Members

It is not always easy to draw the boundaries of the team. In addition to those directly involved in care of the patient and family (the 'inner' team), there is an 'outer' team without which the 'inner' team could not function effectively. The 'outer' team includes domestics, kitchen staff, porters, receptionists, secretaries and administrators. Thus, when considering the nature and functioning of a team, the contributions and needs of both groups should be included. All too often, however, team meetings are limited to the 'inner' team, and the contribution of the 'outer' team is not integrated, and its needs are forgotten.

> At one hospice, a cat visited cat-happy patients. He became particularly attached to one patient. When Frank became very ill, the cat moved from his usual position at Frank's feet to lie across his shoulders - like a fur collar. After Frank's death, the cat sat for days crying outside the room where Frank had died. Three weeks later, when obviously declining, the cat was found to have diabetes. He was taken to the vet to be put down. He was greatly missed by everybody and there was unbridled grief among the kitchen and domestic staff. Emotions which had been held in check in relation to the deaths of patients were precipitated by the death of a cat.

In many hospices, the senior administration is provided by a small group comprising medical director, senior nurse/matron, and administrator/bursar. The latter, however, is not directly involved in the care of patients and families. Nurses have their own management structure and relationships, as do doctors. Thus, there is likely to be a series of 'mini-teams' which corporately comprise the total team. Some people will be members of several 'mini-teams':

- senior administration
- general administration, secretaries, telephonists and receptionists
- house-keeping and catering
- nurses
- doctors
- physiotherapist and occupational therapist
- pastoral care (chaplaincy)
- volunteers
- home care team
- day care team
- inpatient care team
- bereavement support team
- education and training
- research.

And in the community:

- informal carers
- night sitting service
- primary care team (general practitioner, district nurse, health visitor)
- school nurses
- local clergy
- home helps
- fund raisers
- drivers (transportation volunteers).

Volunteers are an important part of a hospice team. They bring a measure of informality and normality into the situation. Their talents are many and include:

- offering a sympathetic ear
- providing companionship for someone who is sad, lonely, or isolated
- providing the practical means to achieve goals
- bringing creativity in place of boredom or frustration.

Some volunteers offer help with administrative and housekeeping tasks.

The core clinical team (the 'inner' team) most commonly comprises nurse, doctor, social worker, counsellor and clergyman. Although each profession has a specific contribution to make, there are inevitably areas of overlap. This is particularly true of the more broadly-based professions of nursing and medicine. 'Role-blurring' is, therefore, an inevitable feature of teamwork [3] (Figure 1).

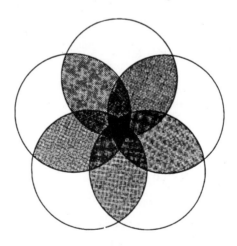

Figure 1 Each circle represents a different profession. The shaded areas indicate the overlap in tasks and roles which occurs in teamwork

Nurse

Nurses often act as the coordinators of care for the dying person and family because of frequent and prolonged contact with them, and knowledge of and access to health care resources. There are numerous nursing problems associated with dying, particularly when the person becomes weaker and is unable to carry out the normal activities of daily living. Nurses have also traditionally been the professional carers who come alongside and stay with those who are ill, caring until and beyond death.

Doctor

Doctors are responsible for the assessment and treatment of pain and other symptoms. A wide variety of specialist backgrounds is represented among hospice doctors including general practice, general internal medicine, radiotherapy, oncology, anaesthetics, surgery. The common denominator is a deeply felt concern for improving the quality of life of dying people and their families.[4] In 1987, the Joint Committee on Higher Medical Training recognized and approved a training programme for a speciality of palliative medicine.[6]

Social worker

Social workers emphasize that every dying person is part of a social system which influences how they will deal with the illness. They focus on the family and contribute on both psychological and practical levels. Because of skills in helping others explore and express thoughts and feelings which may be difficult and painful, and by accepting and tolerating uncomfortable feelings, social workers also have a specific role in supporting the team itself.

Counsellor

In most hospices, nurses, doctors, social worker and chaplain between them provide a counselling service for the patients and families. Indeed, many see this additional function as part of the attraction of hospice work, in that it affords an opportunity to practise a wider range of skills than is generally possible.

Some hospices, however, have the services of staff who have specific training in counselling. Others may have a clinical psychologist or a psychiatrist as a member of the team. As with the social worker, these will have a specific contribution to make in terms of team support.

Chaplain

Chaplains attend to both spiritual and religious needs which arise as people search for meaning in this final phase. Besides working with dying people and families, chaplains may also be an important source of support and encouragement to other team members.

The unique areas and the areas of overlap vary from profession to profession. At the centre of Figure 1, there is an area of total overlap which represents the area which any team member, with training and experience, should be able to respond to. This will include 'being there' and active listening (see chapters 8, 10 and 11). This central area relates to our common humanity. All carers have specific 'tickets of entry' into a relationship with patients and their families. However functional that relationship may initially be, it has the potential for growth into a mutual exploration of the meaning of life and death, and of other fundamental issues.

Shared Purpose

Having a common purpose unifies. Yet, although the overall goal of the highest possible quality of life for the dying person may be easily agreed, consensus about what constitutes good quality life may be more difficult to achieve. One advantage of teamwork is that living and dying are perceived more comprehensively than is usually the case in an isolated professional context. The situation is approached as a whole rather than from the limited perspective of an individual discipline. When the understanding of each professional is placed alongside the understanding or perspective of others, there is less risk that a problem will be missed or misdiagnosed and either mistreated or left untreated.[7]

A distinctive fact of hospice history bears on the issue of sharing a common purpose. The founders of many hospices were inspired by Christian beliefs and attracted like-minded staff to work with them. As the number of hospices grew, staff and volunteers have come increasingly from all faiths and none. Whereas in the beginning a shared understanding could be taken for granted within a Christian framework, this can no longer be assumed. One area where differences within a team may arise will be in the exploration of spiritual issues with the dying person. This may lead to uncertainty, for example, about the manner in which spiritual support can be offered by those other than the clergy.

One strength of a team is the ability of different members to support as and when appropriate.[8] This enhances flexibility but the concomitant blurring of roles can create the need to negotiate who does what in any given situation. In hospice care, the patient and family are seen as parts of the team, participating in the setting of goals and priorities, and sharing in decisions about management (see chapter 10).

Each team member brings not only a working self but also a personal self reflected in values, styles of working and experiences. Thus, each team is unique even when composed of similar professional groups. It is this unique combination of individuals that gives teamwork a fascinating complexity.

A factor which affects the way a team functions is how much experience members have of working in a team. Most professional training programmes do not include specific preparation for working as part of a multi-professional team. In most health care settings, 'parallel practice' would accurately describe professional interactions. Thus, the experience of teamwork which most new staff members bring to a hospice is what is found in most acute care settings, namely:

- hierarchical relationships
- isolated practice
- the absence of partnership with patients.

Group Consciousness

When members begin to adapt to each other and find the appropriate place for themselves, both professionally and personally, the sense emerges within the team that a whole has been created out of the various parts. Constructive working together develops over time and may emerge through a pattern of four phases: [9]

- 'forming'
- 'storming'
- 'norming'
- 'performing'.

These four phases will include uncomfortable times as individual members explore, both personally and together, questions which focus on group dynamics as well as issues relating to the task itself (Table 1).

Table 1   Group development

Phase	Group structure	Task activity
Forming	Members experience anxiety as they seek to discover the nature of the situation, the help that can be expected from the leader and the behaviour that will or will not be appropriate	What is the task? Members seek the answer to this basic question, as well as the rules and the methods to be employed to accomplish the task
Storming	Conflict emerges between sub-groups; authority and/or competency of the leader is challenged; opinions polarize; individuals react against efforts of the leader or group to control them	The value and feasibility of the task is questioned; people react emotionally against its demands
Norming	The group begins to harmonize; it experiences cohesion or unity for the first time; norms emerge as those in conflict are reconciled and resistance is overcome; mutual support develops	Co-operation on the task begins; plans are made; work-standards laid down; communication of views and feelings develop
Performing	The group structures itself or accepts a structure which fits its common task most appropriately. Roles are seen in terms of the task, and flexibility between members develops	Constructive work on the task moves ahead; progress is experienced as the group's energy is applied to its common task.

Adapted from Adair 1986 [9]

Team development requires members to deal with relationships between themselves. Experience suggests that social gatherings and celebrations facilitate the process of developing open relationships. Interpersonal involvement is greater in a team which relies on the use of 'self' in the offered care. Working through uncomfortable feelings, therefore, is a prerequisite before a team's resources and energy can be fully focused on the task.

The addition or the loss of a team member changes the group dynamics and the team is forced to re-adjust. Conflicts will inevitably arise. Paradoxically, although hospice staff are often able to help dying patients and their families resolve conflicts, they often have difficulty confronting the conflicts which arise among themselves.

Many people, regardless of the social context, find direct expression of feelings difficult, particularly negative ones. In hospice work, some team members interpret offering support to include sharing only positive experiences and feelings, i.e. 'being nice' to each other. Acknowledging and dealing together with the full range of feelings may be socially difficult and evoke a sense of personal vulnerability and discomfort. Sharing together both the good and the difficult is necessary, however, to develop open, flexible and mature relationships.

Interdependence

Mutual dependence enhances a feeling of support and security as the contribution of each member is understood and esteemed by the others. Energy can be directed towards achieving a shared goal, and the otherwise oppressive sense of full responsibility for meeting the needs of the dying person and family is shared and better met.

Interdependence, however, tests the more usual ways of working. Potential demands on team members include:

- the need to share information about the patient and family within the boundaries of confidentiality
- competition and jealousy among team members provoked when the patient and family choose to use a specific team member as the key person to share information and feelings
- self-revelation and the need to communicate and deal openly with feelings
- peer scrutiny and evaluation, particularly by those outside one's discipline
- feeling submerged in a group and thus having to cope with the loss of a unique professional identity.[3]

The team and confidentiality

Teamwork presents a potential problem in relation to confidentiality. Should **everything** which the patient shares with one member of the team automatically become the common property of the team? At Burrswood, a Christian residential healing centre, for example, it is routine during the initial medical assessment for the doctor to explain to the patient how a multiprofessional team works. It is explained that the patient is included as a member of the team whenever practicable. Further, that whatever is shared by the patient with any member of the team will be the property of the team, but that the team as a whole is a totally confidential group. If the patient shares something with a team member which he/ she wishes should go no further than the particular team member, then the patient only has to say "Keep that to yourself." The 'restricted information' is not recorded in writing nor passed on verbally. This 'team confidentiality' is accepted by patients, and the fact that the issue has been discussed brings its own sense of security and confidence.

The potential of a team

Being in a team does not reduce the work involved, though it may enhance the quality of care. A team approach to care is rightly commended but the stresses of team work are frequently not understood. Difficulties have to be acknowledged and creatively struggled with. The tantalizing picture which the New Testament paints of the Kingdom of God seems to speak directly to this challenge. For that too is a time or state when hierarchies and systems of power which previously seemed all-important are overturned. Working with the dying in the hospice constantly reminds us that it is frequently not the most senior person who is empowered by the patient and by circumstances to minister and to mediate healing.

Other problems may arise when the considerable needs of the dying are compared with one's own needs in such a way as to trivialize the latter, and thereby encourage a team member to give excessively, particularly of time. The team can help to set the limits necessary to prevent the exhaustion which may render one of its members less effective, and vulnerable to feelings of inadequacy and guilt (see chapter 12). The impact of not setting limits extends beyond team members to their families. The team can help the individual member to resist the temptation not to set limits by exploring realistic and appropriate responses in the context of seemingly unlimited needs.[10]

One benefit of teamwork should be an increasing repertoire of strategies based on collective experience to deal with the range of problems which occur when caring for dying people. Other potential benefits include:

- increased knowledge
- more job satisfaction
- higher morale
- lower sickness rate.

Structures that Support Teamwork

Conflict is bound to arise in teamwork. Indeed, if there is no conflict, there is almost certainly no true teamwork, merely 'parallel professional practice'. Any team needs to consider the responses and roles enacted by different team members as they meet and work together.

It may be accepted at a formal level that the senior nurse or medical director should lead the team, and this may well work out in practice if the person concerned has the knowledge and ability to facilitate team meetings. A team tends to produce its leader as a result of group dynamics.

A forum is needed both to make decisions about care and to manage stress and conflict. The traditional way of working requires the doctor to be the team leader for the professional carers. Some teams are comfortable with this. But other teams may want to develop other ways. It may require considerable effort, however, to break down conventional, status-determined patterns.[4] Familiarity with group dynamics and the causes and manifestations of stress related to care of the dying often help a team meet the challenges which arise within it.[2,11]

If the traditional hierarchical relationships are to be modified, it is important to define the responsibilities of the team leader. These are distinct from those of the employer or manager, though they may be combined. The team leader may be of equal status professionally with the other members, but allocated particular tasks for the good of the team as a whole. Qualities desirable in a team leader include:

- ability to listen to the team and each member
- sensitivity in handling conflict and problems
- objectivity and discipline
- skill in negotiating

- moral courage to take decisions even if unpopular
- ability to monitor and safeguard team welfare.

Obviously, the leader must command the respect of the team and those to whom the team is answerable.

The two components of teamwork, namely, decision-making and stress and conflict management, are sometimes handled successfully in the same setting. Often, however, it is necessary to allocate separate times to work through these distinct tasks. The primary task of the team is to provide care and support to dying people and their families. If the demands of team support threaten this primary task, the team may require outside help. Some teams make regular use of an outside facilitator, i.e. someone who is not normally part of the team. Whatever approach is used, review of team functioning is helpful. The content of team review will arise from:

- the processes of clinical management
- care evaluation
- personal responses to the dying.

It is essential to build trust and mutual respect, personally and as a team, from the review process. It does not happen easily or rapidly:

> "It is naive to bring together a highly diverse group of people and expect that, by calling them a team, they will in fact behave as a team. It is ironic indeed to realize that a football team spends forty hours a week practising teamwork for the two hours on Sunday afternoon when their teamwork really counts. Teams seldom spend two hours per year practising when their ability to function as a team counts forty hours per week."[5]

Conclusion

Working together authentically in a team holds much promise. It requires the skills of:

- establishing and maintaining communication
- negotiation
- acknowledging and handling conflicts.

It is not surprising that teamwork is itself **work** taking time. Nonetheless, the skills can be learned, provided one is willing to allow the painful experience of group dynamics to bring self-knowledge. This, in turn, produces openness, flexibility, and personal growth.

References

1   Parkes CM.   *Bereavement Studies of Grief in Adult Life.* Pelican Books, London 1975.
2   Vachon MLS. *Occupation Stress in the Care of the Critically Ill, the Dying, and the Bereaved.* Hemisphere Publishing Corporation, New York 1987.
3   Vachon MLS.   Battle fatigue in hospice/palliative care.   In: Gilmore A, Gilmore S (eds). *A Safer Death.* Plenum, New York 1988.
4   Dunlop RJ, Hockley JM. *Terminal Care Support Teams.* Oxford University Press, Oxford 1990.
5   Brill N. *Together in the Human Services.* Lippincott, London 1976, 45.
6   Ford G.   Specialist medical training in the UK. *Palliative Medicine* 1988; **2**: 147-152.
7   Cassell EJ.   The Nature of suffering and the goals of medicine. *New England Journal of Medicine* 1982; **306**: 639-645.
8   Schumacher FE. *Good Work.* Cape, London 1979.
9   Adair J. *Effective Teambuilding.* Gower, London 1986.
10 Tuckwell G. The Caring Community. *Healing and Wholeness* 1991; **1**: 38-41.
11 Bion WR. *Experiences in Groups.* Tavistock, London 1959.

10 NURSING AND MEDICAL ASPECTS OF CARE

"To cure sometimes,
to relieve often,
to comfort always."

Nursing and medical care are developed expressions of a natural caring response to physical or mental distress by fellow human beings. Both are essentially practical; a potential or actual problem is perceived, assessed and responded to. This 'problem-oriented' approach is well illustrated by Tolstoy in his novel '*Anna Karenina*'. Shortly before Nicholas dies of tuberculosis, he is visited by his brother, Levin, and sister-in-law, Kitty. Levin is revolted by his brother's debilitated condition and finds himself unable to do anything. On the other hand, Kitty, with an intuitive insight as to what is needed, rolls up her sleeves and proceeds to wash, reclothe, make comfortable and feed the dying man.[1]

A similar response is portrayed in the parable of the compassionate Samaritan:

"A man was on his way from Jerusalem down to Jericho when he was set upon by robbers, who stripped and beat him, and went off leaving him half dead...But a Samaritan who was going that way came upon him, and when he saw him he was moved to pity. He went up and bandaged his wounds, bathing them with oil and wine. Then he lifted him on to his own beast, brought him to an inn, and looked after him." (Luke 10.30, 33-34)

126

Changing Circumstances

The primitive medications of the past have been replaced by a sophisticated array of treatments - psychological, physical, pharmacological and surgical. Perhaps nothing illustrates this better than the use of antibiotics during the last 50 years.[2] Before antibiotics became available, if someone developed pneumonia, there were several days of high fever during which the patient fought for life against the infection. Everything was done to maintain the patient's strength, but no specific cure existed. Then, after five or six days, the body produced an out-pouring of antibodies into the blood, the skin poured with sweat, the temperature came down and the patient sat up and asked for food. The 'crisis' had come. But often the outcome was death, if apathy or weakness could not match the bacterial invasion.

The treatment of pneumonia changed dramatically with the discovery of antibiotics. Its cure now lies in the hands of the doctor. In the past, it was common to pray for the healing of a patient with pneumonia. Earnest intercession for the patient was made day after day by families and congregations, until the crisis or death came. Today we do not need to pray for the crisis; penicillin is given and it comes. Even very old people can be saved repeatedly from death by pneumonia.

As a result, our understanding of the relationship of God to a person with pneumonia has changed. It is as if God has put the responsibility for life or death into human hands. Pneumonia has been taken off the intercession list and put on the thanksgiving list instead. In practice, however, God has totally slipped out of our thinking in relation to pneumonia.

Unfortunately, it is often not just God who tends to slip out of our thinking but also the person as well. The facts and explanations, the diagnosis and the cure, can all be given in terms of bacteriology, pathology and pharmacology. Unless we are people who like to ask a deeper 'Why?', we do not have to look further.

When nurses and doctors practise within a highly scientific framework, there is a tendency for care to become less personal. For example, it is all too easy for the nurses to become pre-occupied with:

● administering medication
● routine observations (pulse, temperature, etc.)
● specimen collection (sputum, urine, etc.).

Task-oriented nursing and 'high-tech' medicine tend to lead to barriers between the professional and the patient. Thus, there is need for nurses and doctors, and other health-care workers, to remember their antecedents and always to seek to be 'skilled companions' (see chapter 1). All of us when ill need fully personal care, not just the dying.

Ethos of Cure and Ethos of Care

Halina Bortnowska, a Polish philosopher, author and sometime hospice volunteer, has contrasted the **ethos of cure** with the **ethos of care**. She defines ethos as a constellation of values held by people. The ethos of cure is disease-centred and embraces the military virtues of fighting, not giving up and endurance. It necessarily contains a measure of hardness. In contrast, the ethos of care is person-centred and has human dignity as its central value. It stresses the solidarity between the patient and the carers, an attitude which results in 'effective compassion'. In curing 'the physician is the general', whereas in caring 'the patient is the sovereign'.

It is important not to allow the authoritarian approach appropriate in acute medical and surgical emergencies to take over in other situations. Because basic professional training concentrates to a large extent on coping with emergencies, nurses and doctors all too easily adopt an authoritarian approach all the time. Apart from life-and-death situations, however, nurses and doctors should not expect instant and total patient compliance. Care plans and treatment should normally be offered, not imposed. Options should be stated, adapted if necessary, and priorities agreed. This does not mean it is necessarily wrong for nurses and doctors to be directive. Their professional knowledge gives them a greater awareness than most patients of the physical, and sometimes the psychosocial, implications of the disease. But it is nearly always possible to share this knowledge in plain English so that the patient's autonomy is respected and decisions about goals and treatment can be made jointly.

Pain and Suffering

The relief of suffering is one of the primary aims of medicine. But what suffering is and what nurses and doctors must do to prevent and relieve it is often poorly understood. Because of this, the best-trained and most well-intentioned nurses and doctors may cause suffering inadvertently and unnecessarily in the course of treating disease.[3]

Pain and suffering are distinct phenomena. In consequence, suffering must be distinguished from pain or other symptoms with which it may be associated. For example, a patient may tolerate severe pain without considering herself to be suffering if she knows:

- the cause of the pain
- that it can be dealt with
- that it will be relatively short-lived.

On the other hand, even relatively minor symptoms may cause suffering if they are believed or known to:

- have a life-threatening cause
- be intractable
- reflect a hopeless prognosis.

Indeed, suffering may occur in the absence of any symptoms, e.g. when witnessing the physical deterioration of a loved one.

Suffering is experienced by persons, not by bodies. It stems from a threat to the integrity of the person as a complex social and psychological entity.[4] Helplessness is a potent source of suffering.

Case History

A 35-year old sculptress with widespread breast cancer was treated by doctors employing advanced knowledge and technology and acting with kindness and true concern. But, at every stage, the treatment as well as the disease was a source of suffering to her.

For example, she had not realized that the irradiated breast would be so disfiguring. After the removal of her ovaries and the prescription of hormones, she became hirsute, obese, and devoid of libido. When the cancer spread to her neck, she lost strength in the hand she used for sculpting. Such a profound loss of creative potential resulted in deep depression. She sustained a pathological fracture of the femur, and treatment was delayed while her doctors openly disagreed about the advisability of pinning it. She was uncertain and frightened about her future.

Each time there was a response to treatment and her hope rekindled, there would be a subsequent new manifestation of disease. Thus, when a new course of chemotherapy was started, she was torn between a desire to live and the fear that, if she allowed hope to rekindle, she would once again be devastated when the treatment failed.

She feared the future. Each tomorrow was seen as heralding increased sickness, pain, or disability, never as the beginning of better times. She felt isolated because she was no longer like other people and could not do what others did. She feared that her friends would stop visiting her. She was sure that she was going to die.[4]

This account emphasizes that:

- a disease of this kind is devastating in its impact on the patient
- suffering may be caused both by the disease and its treatment
- suffering is not limited to physical symptoms
- in order to identify sources of suffering, it is necessary to listen to the patient and ask open questions (see p 136).

This woman's suffering extended to threats to social and private spheres in that she suffered from the effects of both the disease and its treatment on her appearance and abilities, and from her perception of the future.

A Human Dimension

Perhaps the major challenge facing nurses and doctors in an economically rich country such as Britain is how to achieve and maintain a human dimension in professional care. It has been suggested that few doctors employ the common courtesy of shaking hands with a patient when meeting for the first time in a hospital consultation room.

There is, however, a continuing difficulty. When viewed only from the aspect of professional knowledge and skill, a client-professional relationship is bound to be unequal. But when viewed from the aspect of their common humanity, the client-professional relationship is equal.[5] Whether the professional is put 'on a pedestal' or not, and whether the professional finds a pedestal congenial or not, is an inter-personal matter, not one of knowledge and skill. These are matters of personality and personal relationship. Two personalities, often very different in their use of authority, are involved in this interaction. Both nurses and doctors need to be aware of their own use of authority, and to respect the patient's mode of behaviour.

The context for a client-professional relationship is always their common humanity. Both patients and health-care professionals (sometimes one taking the lead, sometimes the other) need to work towards an increasingly mature interpersonal relationship which can give to both an interdependent dignity, and also sustain the differences of their knowledge and skill. Nurses, doctors, patients and families are all, first and foremost, human beings; of whom some happen to be sick and others happen to be specially trained.

> "Whatever kind of professional expertise or experience one may be equipped with, the first requirement in any encounter is that one should approach it as if it were totally novel."[6]

Enhancing the Patient's Self-Esteem

When thrust by adverse circumstances into the role of a patient, most people feel:

- that they have lost control over their lives
- extremely vulnerable and disadvantaged.

Nurses and doctors need to recognize this and do all they can to enhance a patient's self-esteem. Thus, in their dealings with a patient, nurses and doctors must:

- be courteous
- avoid patronizing behaviour
- listen
- provide a clear explanation of the cause of the illness and the associated symptoms
- (doctors) discuss treatment options
- (nurses) discuss necessary personal care
- respect the patient's decision to decline or modify treatment and/or care recommendations
- allow the patient to retain as much control as possible in chronic and terminal illness
- show a commitment to ongoing support
- foster hope.

Some research in counselling suggests that three qualities are needed in the therapist if a relationship is to be therapeutic for a client: [7]

- empathy, i.e. the ability to sense correctly what someone else is feeling but not necessarily expressing (e.g. anger or anxiety)
- warmth, i.e. a warm outgoing feeling towards others, with a non-judgemental acceptance of all that they reveal themselves to be
- genuineness, i.e. trustworthiness, openness, and a wholesomeness of character which is real and not a professional facade.

The same attitudes and values are necessary in nurses and doctors if they wish to offer maximum support to patients and their families.

1. Be courteous

Because of the constraints of time, it is easy for nurses and doctors to ignore the common courtesies which they would employ automatically under other circumstances, and which do much to express consideration and esteem for the individuality of another person. Nurses and doctors must remind themselves not to by-pass the basic essentials:

- introduce oneself by name ('Good morning, Mrs Smith, I am Dr Jones')
- shake hands if appropriate (Note: male orthodox Jews and male Muslims would be deeply offended if obliged to shake hands with a woman)
- sit down on chair or bed ('Is it all right if I sit on the edge of your bed?')
- make eye to eye contact.

2. Avoid patronizing behaviour

Although first names are used fairly widely nowadays, nurses and doctors should not assume that this is what a patient would like. To use first names automatically is belittling for many people, particularly if the privilege is not mutual. Many patients, however, feel uncomfortable calling a doctor or senior nurse by his or her first name. For some there is a definite need to maintain 'professional distance'.

Care must be taken to avoid the 'Does he take sugar?' syndrome. This refers to the habit of talking in the patient's presence to a third person as if the patient is incapable of answering for herself. 'Talking down' to patients must also be avoided.

Case History

> Kate suspected she had lung cancer. When she asked
> the doctors at the hospital whether this was the case,
> "They patted me on the head, like a little girl, and told
> me not to worry". Some months later she opened a
> sealed letter she was asked to deliver to a general
> practitioner. The letter referred to the presence of
> advanced incurable cancer and went on to say, "The
> daughter knows, but we decided it would be better not
> to tell the patient." Kate was furious and felt humiliated.
> It was her body and her life; and yet she was being kept
> in the dark, being treated as if she were a child or totally
> incompetent.[8]

To say 'Don't worry' in answer to a patient's question is a
self-protective reflex which is both bad psychology and
belittling. Although seemingly well-intentioned, it is:

● felt by the patient as a 'put-down'
● fails to resolve the patient's concern
● heightens the patient's anxiety and distress
● serves as a barrier to open communication.

3.   Listen to the patient

It is remarkable that, in general, psychological assessment
and communication skills are still inadequately taught to
nursing and medical students. It is encouraging that, *inter
alia*, the Council of Europe has recognized this deficiency
and is urging member states to rectify the situation.

There are many barriers to open communication.[9] A desperate
need in the nurse or doctor to make everything 'all right' is
a powerful one. An opening comment such as:

> 'You do look better today!'

may well prevent the patient from expressing negative feelings and worries. To begin with a positive comment such as:

'Hullo, Mrs Smith, it's good to see you again'

is fine provided the patient is then 'given permission' through an open question to express negative feelings if she wishes to:

'What sort of a night did you have?'
'How are things today?'
'How is your world today?'

Even so, an open question, 'How are you feeling?' may still elicit the reflex answer, 'Fine, thank you, nurse'. This can be guarded against by saying:

'Right - now let's start again. I'll ask you the question, and this time you tell me the truth.'

It is important, however, to try to end on a positive note:

'This is what we need to do to improve the situation...'
'I shall see you again on Friday; I look forward to seeing you then.'

All nurses and doctors need to be able to 'listen actively'.[10] For example:

- take the initiative and give the patient permission to talk about feelings and fears by using open questions such as those above
- nod from time to time to show that you are paying attention
- if the patient stops mid-sentence, repeat the last three words. This gives the patient permission to go on, and the offer is rarely declined
- pick up on 'throw-away' comments, e.g. 'It's like Granny's illness' and 'No, I haven't got any pain - yet'

- summarize what the patient has said to confirm that you have heard correctly
- listen for what is not said:
  - but what experience would lead you to expect
  - who is not mentioned
  - mismatch between words and non-verbal behaviour (as in the poem on p 138: verse 2, line 3).

"Techniques of listening and communication are only the beginning; human experience has to fill out the whole".[11]

4. Explanation

Treatment begins with an explanation by the doctor of the cause of the illness and the reason(s) for particular symptoms. The patient is reassured to learn that the doctor understands what is happening. This reduces the threat to the patient and thereby reduces suffering. If explanation is omitted, the patient continues to think that his condition is shrouded in mystery. This is frightening ('Even the doctors don't know what is going on!'). It poses an additional threat and so increases the patient's suffering.

Case History

A 55 year-old man with recently diagnosed cancer of the oesophagus was still in pain despite receiving a total of **12g** of morphine a day. Following admission to a hospice, he became pain-free on **60mg** a day and a tranquillizer at bedtime. He returned home, converted the spare bedroom into a workshop, and was able to spend many happy hours there. The key to success was **listening, explaining** and **setting goals**.[12]

I huddle warm inside my corner bed,
Watching the other patients sipping tea.
I wonder why I'm so long getting well,
And why it is no one will talk to me.

The nurses are so kind. They brush my hair
On days I feel too ill to read or sew.
I smile and chat, try not to show my fear,
They cannot tell me what I want to know.

The visitors come in. I see their eyes
Become embarrassed as they pass my bed.
"What lovely flowers" they say, then hurry on
In case their faces show what can't be said.

The chaplain passes on his weekly round
With friendly smile and calm, untroubled brow.
He speaks with deep sincerity of life.
I'd like to speak of death, but don't know how.

The surgeon comes, with student retinue,
Mutters to Sister, deaf to my silent plea.
I want to tell this dread I feel inside,
But they are all too kind to talk to me.[13]

Explanation is particularly important when the patient is at home because of the additional responsibility which family members have in relation to providing care and comfort. Explanations generally need to be repeated. This responsibility usually falls to the nurse, who may need to encourage the patient to repeat what she was told in order to validate or correct it. The implications of the new information may also need to be explored together. At some centres, when bad news is to be given, the interview is taped and the tape given to the patient for her to listen to with her family at home, if she wishes.

5. Discuss treatment options and care plans and agree on action

It is often appropriate to discuss treatment options with the patient and to decide together on the immediate course of action. In this respect, the patient (and family) is an integral part of the team (see chapter 9). Few things are more demeaning to a person's self-esteem than to be disregarded in discussions concerning treatment. It is hurtful when a doctor ignores the patient and treats her as of no account. On the other hand, it is equally important that the doctor does not force the patient to make decisions for which the doctor should take responsibility.

Some patients may wish to have continuing, aggressive, anti-cancer treatment despite the probability that it will do more harm than good. Although the doctor may prefer not to offer such treatments, there are occasions when it is appropriate to comply with the patient's wishes. Other patients may reject surgery or radiotherapy and opt for alternative or complementary therapies, even after explanation that, for example, a breast cancer is likely to break through the skin if not given specific local treatment. The doctor must control his frustration that an effective treatment is being rejected and remain courteous, friendly and supportive to the patient, who will appreciate the respect accorded to her wishes.

In relation to nursing care, it is important to negotiate when this is given. Explanation is a necessary preliminary to negotiation; otherwise the patient cannot make an informed choice. Often quite small things make all the difference; for example, a patient might prefer a bath later rather than earlier in the morning. Another may object to the nurses' obsession with cleanliness and decline to have a bath more than once a week. Some patients object to the use of rectal suppositories and enemas in the treatment of constipation. Here again, although there may be scope for negotiation, their distaste for rectal measures should be respected in all but the most extreme situations. Likewise, if a patient declines to eat, his choice should be respected - provided it is a considered decision and not based on misunderstanding.

The current moves towards 'primary nursing' in hospitals and hospices should help in this respect.[14] With primary nursing two or three nurses provide all aspects of nursing care for each patient, whereas with the more traditional pattern of hospital nursing each task might well be delegated to a different member of the nursing team. Thus, primary nursing facilitates:

- continuity of care
- flexibility in care
- more individual care.

The potential for person-to-person relationships and partnership in care is considerably greater with primary nursing and is clearly something that should be encouraged.

Discussion with close relatives gives the opportunity to enlist their cooperation and to reinforce symptom-control plans. If actively involved in supporting the patient they have a right to be informed, subject to the patient's approval. It is important, however, not to let the relatives 'take over'. Those who are seriously ill and the dying have a right to be treated for what they usually are: sane, sensible adults. In this connection, it is important to recognize the hierarchy of relationships. When there is conflict between the patient and the family about disclosure of information and treatment decisions, the patient's wishes are paramount.

6. Allow the patient to retain control

Allowing the patient to retain control is an important way of maintaining the patient's self-esteem. In addition to negotiating treatment and care plans (rather than imposing), there is a variety of ways in which a patient may be enabled to exercise control. For example:

- take time to help the patient adjust to the system (who, what, when, why, how?)
- involvement in decision-making to a level the patient decides
- the patient sets the order of priorities and determines the approach adopted
- permitting self-medication
- ability to **choose**, e.g. food, clothes, activities, visitors, rest hour
- ability to **contribute**, e.g. washing up, weeding, delivering mail or newspapers.

7. A commitment to ongoing support

The basic message a patient wants to hear at a time of increasing uncertainty is:

> 'We will not abandon you.'
> 'You are important to us.'

Only part of this can be said in words:

'We will continue to take good care of you.'

'I will see you regularly.'

'One of us will always be available.'

'We can anticipate many of the problems which may arise, but if you have questions or an unforeseen problem arises, you can contact us by telephoning...'

For the most part, however, the message is conveyed by actions. For example, with patients at home, it is important to make a definite next appointment:

'I shall call in and see you again on Tuesday, roundabout 12 o'clock. Will that be all right?'

It is important to avoid the 'plumber mentality':

'If you've got a problem, give me a call and I'll be right round to fix it.'

Such an approach is generally not supportive. Many patients and families do not telephone for help or advice because they are reluctant to be 'a nuisance'. As noted in chapter 1, a planned regular visit once a week (or even a telephone call) can make all the difference. The fact that the visit or call is not dependent on there being a problem to resolve makes it more supportive.

8. Foster hope

Although the focus of hope changes with age and circumstances,[15] nurses and doctors can foster hope in their patients by:

- enhancing self-esteem (see above)
- demonstrating a commitment to ongoing support (see above)
- setting specific treatment goals
- relieving pain and other distressing symptoms.

Hope needs an object. Setting realistic goals jointly with the patient is one way of restoring and maintaining hope. This can be initiated, for example, by asking the patient:

'And what do you hope will come out of this consultation?'

An agreed order of priorities can then be established. It is sometimes necessary to advise the patient that wanting to be cured is unrealistic, certainly as an immediate goal. It may be necessary to break down an ultimate and possibly unrealistic goal into a series of more realistic 'mini-goals'.

Goal-setting is an integral part of caring for those with chronic diseases, including terminal cancer. It has been shown that nurses and doctors in hospices set significantly more goals than their counterparts in a general hospital.[15]

In patients close to death, hope becomes re-focused on 'being' rather than 'doing', and emphasizes relationships - with others and with God (or a 'higher being').[16] In consequence, it is possible for hope to increase as death approaches. (Hope is discussed further in chapter 11.)

Touch

Touch is the means by which we express our essential connectedness, our common humanity.[17] This explains why touch is culturally conditioned; it is a fundamental and powerful symbol.

Within the context of nursing and medical care, touch can be distinguished but not necessarily separated into 'instrumental' and 'expressive'. Instrumental touch refers to touch as part of a nursing or medical task, e.g. changing a dressing or measuring blood pressure. Expressive touch has been described as 'caring touch'.[18] Expressive touch is extremely supportive to the patient, and can enhance physical healing and general well-being. In 'Anatomy of an Illness', the author writes of:

"The utter void created by the longing - ineradicable, unremitting, pervasive - for warmth of human contact. A warm smile and an outstretched hand were valued even above the offerings of modern science, but the latter were far more accessible than the former." [19]

One nurse observed that there are two kinds of doctor:

"Beside-the-bed doctors, who [are] interested in the patient, and foot-of-the-bed doctors, who [are] interested in the patient's condition." [20]

Yet, despite the benefits of expressive touch, "most of the medical profession like to keep their dehumanizing distance." [21] Such a criticism is also true of many nurses (see opposite).

Demented and disturbed patients in a psychogeriatric ward have been noted to respond positively to touch, e.g. hand-holding and stroking. [22] It is encouraging, therefore, that there is an increasing interest among nurses in the use of massage in patient care, particularly for the chronic sick, the elderly and the dying. [23]

Cultural differences are obviously important, particularly because touch commonly has a sexual connotation. It is generally acceptable to place an arm around the shoulders of a grieving person, but it would be offensive to most Arab and Asian women. Sensitivity is clearly needed in the use of touch. There are occasions when it may be therapeutic **not** to touch. For example, when someone begins to cry, touching may not only stop the tears but also the associated verbal expression of negative emotions. Rushing in to comfort by touching tends to convey the message all too often learned in

Death in the First Person

"I am a student nurse. I am dying. I write this to you who are, and will become, nurses in the hope that by my sharing my feelings with you, you may someday be better able to help those who share my experience.

For me, fear is today and dying is now. You slip in and out of my room, give me medications and check my blood pressure. Is it because I am a student nurse myself, or just a human being, that I sense your fright? And your fears enhance mine. Why are you afraid? I am the one who is dying!

Death may get to be a routine to you, but it is new to me. You may not see me as unique, but I've never died before. To me, once is pretty unique! You whisper about my youth, but when one is dying, is one really so young anymore? I have lots I wish we could talk about. It really would not take much more of your time because you are in here quite a bit anyway.

If only we could be honest, both admit our fears, touch one another. If you really care, would you lose so much of your valuable professionalism if you even cried with me? Just person to person? Then, it might not be so hard to die - in a hospital - with friends close by."[24]

childhood, 'There, there, don't cry, Mummy's here'. Despite these caveats, touch remains an important therapeutic tool, and its use is to be encouraged.

Respect the Patient as a Person

Most of what has been said in this chapter could be summed up in the sentence: 'Respect the patient as a person'. In our dealings with each other we should aim to meet as adult with adult, and not seek to induce a parent-child relationship.[25] This can sometimes be hard, particularly if we feel as professionals that the patient is adding to his discomfort by a decision to decline our recommendations for nursing care or symptom relief.

Some patients have a deep-rooted objection to 'drugs' and decline all but herbal remedies. Others may refuse any medication that might, even to a modest degree, impair their alertness. As nurses and doctors, we must resist the temptation to 'prettify' death by, for example, using sedative drugs automatically in those close to death. Some patients need to 'die badly'; all should be enabled to do it **their** way.

When I shall die (by ANNA)

"When I shall die,
I shall do it myself.
Nobody shall do it for me.
When I am redy,
I shall say,
'Fin, stand me up',
and I shall look
and lagh merry.
If I fall down,
I shall be dead."[26]

At the End of the Day

Hospice care developed as a reaction to the attitude, spoken or unspoken, that 'There is nothing more that we can do for you' with the inevitable consequence for the patient and family of a sense of abandonment, hopelessness and despair. It was stressed that this was never true - there is always something that can be done. Yet, while this is generally so, there **are** times when a nurse or doctor has nothing specific to do for a patient and, in consequence, feels that she/he has nothing to offer.

In such a situation, we are thrown back on having only ourselves to offer. Sheila Cassidy has illustrated this in a series of sketches:[8]

The first drawing shows the doctor, armed with his competence and his instruments and protected by his aide.

It is the same for the priest performing his sacramental ministry. Here we see him in his stole and dog collar protected by having a role to play and a ritual to perform.

In this drawing we see the patient meeting with either doctor or clergyman when he has exhausted the physical aspects of his ministry. He is left with his hands empty - but with his resources of counselling still available

This last drawing shows both patient and carer stripped of their resources, present to each other, naked and empty handed, as two human beings.

"Slowly, I learn about the importance of powerlessness. I experience it in my own life and I live with it in my work. The secret is not to be afraid of it - not to run away. The dying know we are not God... All they ask is that we do not desert them." [8]

There are circumstances when it is necessary to relinquish the 'Dr Fix-it' and 'Nurse Fix-it' attitudes imbued during training. When there is nothing to offer except ourselves, a belief that life has meaning and purpose helps to sustain the **carers**. We seek to convey the essential message:

"You matter because you are you.
You matter to the last moment of your life,
and we will do all we can
not only to help you die peacefully,
but to live until you die." [27]

References

1   Tolstoy LN. *Anna Karenina*. Penguin Books, London 1969.
2   Wilson M. *A Coat of Many Colours: Pastoral Studies of the Christian Way of Life*. Epworth, London 1988, pp 8-9.
3   Cassell EJ. The relief of suffering. *Archives of Internal Medicine* 1983; **143**: 522-523.
4   Cassell EJ. The nature of suffering and the goals of medicine. *New England Journal of Medicine* 1982; **306**: 639-645.
5   Campbell AV. *Paid to Care? The Limits of Professionalism in Pastoral Care*. SPCK, London 1985.
6   Mathers JR. Book Review. *Hospital Chaplain* 1986, September, p 22.
7   Truax C & Carkhuff R. *Toward Effective Counselling*. Aldine, Chicago 1967.
8   Cassidy S. *Sharing the Darkness*. Darton, Longman & Todd, London 1988, pp 61-64.
9   Maguire P. Barriers to psychological care of the dying. *British Medical Journal* 1985; **291**: 1711-1713.
10 Long A. *Listening*. Darton, Longman & Todd, London 1990.
11 Scott T. Personal communication, 1990.
12 Twycross RG, Lack SA. *Oral Morphine in Advanced Cancer*. Beaconsfield Publishers, Beaconsfield 1989.
13 Anonymous. In: Twycross RG. *The Dying Patient*. CMF Publications, London 1975.
14 Pearson A. *Primary Nursing*. Croom Helm, London 1988.
15 Herth K. Fostering hope in terminally-ill people. *Journal of Advanced Nursing* 1990; **15**: 1250-1259.
16 Lunt B, Neale C. A comparison of hospice and hospital: care goals set by staff. *Palliative Medicine* 1987; **1**: 136-148.
17 Montagu A. *Touching: the Human Significance of the Skin* (2nd Edition). Harper & Row, New York 1978.
18 Autton N. *Touch: An Exploration*. Darton, Longman and Todd, London 1989.
19 Cousins N. *Anatomy of an Illness*. Norton, New York 1979, p 154.
20 Hall E. How cultures collide: an interview with Edward T. Hall. *Psychology Today* 1976; June, p 72.
21 Colton H. *Touch Therapy*. Zebra Books, New York 1988, p 154.
22 Burnside IM. Caring for the aged. *American Journal of Nursing* 1973; **73**: 2060-2063.

23 Sims S. The significance of touch in palliative nursing. *Palliative Medicine* 1988; **2**: 58-61.
24 Anonymous. *American Journal of Nursing* 1970.
25 Harris TA. *I'm OK - You're OK.* Pan, London 1973.
26 Fynn. *Mister God, This is Anna.* Collins, London 1974.
27 Saunders C. From an unpublished lecture.

11 SPIRITUAL AND RELIGIOUS ASPECTS OF CARE

In '*A Way to Die*',[1] the mother says to her 25 year-old daughter dying in a hospice:

> "I don't like the expression 'spiritual', it's too loaded for me, but for want of a better word, I feel that the spiritual part of us is indestructible and emerges again in some form."

As stated in chapter 1, the word 'spiritual' embraces the essence of what it means to be human. It is concerned with 'right-relatedness' and includes those experiences in human life which transcend sensory phenomena. It is often perceived as being concerned with meaning and purpose. One woman dying in her 50s said:

> "You don't realize what a short life you've got. There must be something; you can't go through life for no reason."

Those nearing the end of life commonly feel a need for:

- forgiveness
- reconciliation
- affirmation of worth
- an evaluation of their life, its achievements and failures.

'Spiritual' is often confused with 'religious'. Religious, however, means pertaining to a religion, i.e. a framework of theistic beliefs and rituals which give expression to spiritual concerns. While everyone has a spiritual dimension, in Britain today only a minority practise a formal religion. Hence, although people commonly say, 'I am not religious', they do not say 'I am not spiritual'.

The spiritual dimension transcends and holds together the physical, psychological and social dimensions. The spiritual integrates the other three dimensions into an 'I', an individual who is more than the sum of his parts (Figure 1).

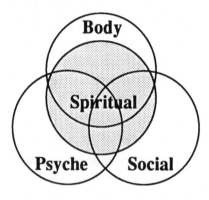

Figure 1. Dimensions of care

Each of the four human dimensions has potential for growth or for atrophy. Many sick, elderly and dying people have already lost many of the things which are important in life to most people, e.g. physical health, home, family, friends, work, recreation. Reduction in one or more dimensions, however, may be compensated by expansion in another. For example, people who are severely limited physically are still intact as human beings. There are many people who enrich their carers despite physical and/or mental disability. The spiritual, therefore, is a possible area of growth as a person lets go of body, mind and social activities. Spiritual care is something which we all give when we give someone our full attention. It is also something which we receive when someone, in turn, gives us that same full attention. I am my neighbour's healer and he is mine.

Spiritual Care is Anchored in the Ordinary

Spiritual care includes very ordinary things. There is, in fact, a range of care which moves from the material and practical (e.g. from offering a cup of cold water) to the formal religious sphere with its sacred writings, prayers and rituals. In the Christian tradition, the sacramental principle speaks of the use of material things as an outward and visible sign by which we receive inward and spiritual grace.   It is important not to despise the material in spiritual care. Since the 1960s colour and furnishings have been seen as important in hospital care. Particularly in psychiatric hospitals, great trouble is now taken to get away from the drab uniform institutional atmosphere of former days, with its dehumanizing influence. Beauty does much for the spirit, and therefore has an important place in spiritual care. For example, bone china cups in a hospice are part of spiritual care, and contrast strikingly with disposable plastic mugs.   Indeed, wherever there is beauty, the spirit will be uplifted:

- paintings
- poetry
- books
- music
- flowers
- countryside
- wilderness
- river, lake, and sea.

One old woman in a newly established hospice was taken in a wheelchair to the patch of wasteland which in time would become the garden. It was her first such outing for many months. "Today", she said, "I tasted the leaves, I smelt the grass".[2]

It must also be remembered that food and its presentation speaks of more than calories and a balanced diet:

> A young woman had surgery, radiotherapy and chemotherapy for cancer. When in hospital for the latter she felt too ill for visits from her clergy. When visited at home she was making bread. As she kneaded the dough, she said, "While I can make bread I know that everything is all right, bread is basic, it sustains life."

Even the cuddly toy seems to have great significance for some people, quite apart from the association with the person who gave or made it.

> "His name is 'Jonathan'. He has known me for eighteen years, in good times and bad. I can hang on to him while I'm having the dressing done."

Being There

> "In some mysterious way
> the quality of my presence, my look
> brings to you life - or death." [3]

One area of spiritual care comes under the heading of the **ministry of presence**, of being there. As someone put it: "It is not theology they want, it's you". Before anything else we are all human beings and, like Christ, the best gift we can offer each other is ourselves. When the boat of life rocks alarmingly, it is good to have someone else there with us. What matters is not being left alone. Metropolitan Anthony Bloom speaks of developing the ability to sit with someone, saying and doing nothing:

> "Not just sitting looking vaguely and vacantly about...

but going deep, so deep in sympathy, in compassion that your presence speaks and, if there is need, you can put your hand on the person and it will mean more than whatever you can say."[4]

This presence puts emphasis on being rather than doing. It is the ability to sit still without feeling guilty or embarrassed. Sometimes, and even at the point of death, people need a physical reminder that the peace and power they call 'God' is there.

Touch is also part of spiritual care. "The nurses hold my hand" said the patient in an intensive care unit after a road accident, "It is better than all the medicine" (see chapter 10).

Sometimes, however, there is need for a 'ministry of absence'. Sick people tire easily or may feel too ill to cope. All carers and visitors must develop a sensitivity to the needs of the patient, and learn when to stay and when to go. If sent away by the patient, it is important to learn not to feel rejected. It is possible to 'hold' the patient in our minds even though physically separated.

Listening

When asked what he most looked for in those caring for him, a patient replied, "For someone to look as if they are trying to understand me". He did not ask for success, but only that someone should care enough to try.[5] Carers offer not only their physical presence, but also their receptivity, their openness, their attention. This involves listening to what people say and what they do not say, and having the wisdom to interpret. It involves acceptance, which may need to include forgiveness.

Sometimes, people can talk only indirectly. For example, a church worker when terminally ill used her Paddington Bear to say the things that she could not allow herself to say directly. Her real feelings were expressed through the bear.

Expressing Anger and Protest

Carers, not least clergy, often have to absorb anger. If someone wants to be angry with God, who better to take it out on than his representatives? One chaplain took an angry woman to the hospital chapel to tell God of her anger. She spoke so softly that she had to be encouraged to shout. Another chaplain tried this but failed when the patient said that she was not on speaking terms with God.

Anger can be creative.[6,7] A West Indian minister tells of the care she tried to give to a young air hostess with cancer. Her father had also died of cancer and now she was terminally ill. The minister was getting nowhere, then one day she told the patient that she was going to pray. And she prayed:

"Lord, you are making a fool of your Church,
you are making a fool of yourself,
and what is more you are making a fool of me!"
"Whatever are you saying?" said the woman.
"I'm cussing it out with the Lord." said the minister.
"Well", said the girl, "If you can talk to him like
that he must be real."

The relationship between the woman and the minister changed as a result of this episode, and the minister was able to provide continuing support until the woman's death.

Forgiveness

God, you need to ask my forgiveness.
Your world is full of mistakes.
Some cells, like weeds in the garden
Are growing in the wrong place.
And we your children
Have polluted our environment.
Why did you let it happen God?
We prayed with faith, hope, love,
We perceived no change in our bodies
    or environment,
We are made sick by your world.
God you need to ask my forgiveness.
Was this why you sent your Son? [8]

The Will of God

'Why' questions may or may not be expressed in religious language, but are asked by both those who have a religious faith and those who have not:

'Why has this happened to me, to him, to her?'
'Why now? Just when we had retired and had so many plans'.
'Why does God allow it?'
'It isn't fair.'
'What have I done to deserve this?'
'What am I being punished for?'

Even some lifelong Christians imagine that the practice of their religion should immunize them against trouble or tragedy. Nowhere, however, are they guaranteed immunity or promised that their lives will be without suffering. In fact the New Testament teaches the opposite:

> "[God] makes his sun rise on good and bad alike, and sends the rain on the honest and the dishonest." (Matt.5.45)

The Service for The Visitation of the Sick in the Book of Common Prayer (1662) has much to answer for in that it states that sickness is the punishment and chastisement of God. This view forgets the quite different perspective on arbitrary suffering elaborated in the Book of Job and confirmed in the teachings of Jesus (Luke 13.1-4).

A common conventional religious reaction is to say 'Thy will be done' or 'It is the will of Allah'. Many people accept this not only as a comment from a third party but suggest it themselves. Some even find comfort in the thought because one cannot argue with the will of God. It is a shorthand expression which people use when wrestling with all manner of negative happenings so bad or so sad that they can only ascribe them to the will of God and accept them without question. Tennyson speaks of this thought-stopping attitude in his poem '*The Village Wife*':[9]

> "Fur hoffens we talkt o'my darter es died
>   o' the fever at fall:
> An' I thowt 'twur the will o' the Lord, but
>   Miss Annie she said it wur draains."

It is perhaps worth noting that 'Thy will be done' is never seen at the bottom of a wedding invitation or the announcement of a birth.

An American pastor said the following in a sermon 10 days after his 24 year-old son was killed by driving his car into Boston Harbour:
Many things can be said when a person dies, but there is at least one thing that should never be said. The night after Alex died I was sitting in the living room of my sister's house outside of Boston when the front door opened and in came a nice-looking middle-aged woman carrying about 18 quiches. When she saw me she shook her head, then headed for the kitchen, saying sadly over her shoulder, "I just don't understand the will of God".

Instantly I was up and in hot pursuit, swarming all over her. "I'll say you don't, lady!" I said. (I knew the anger would do me good, and the instruction to her was long overdue.)

"Do you think it was the will of God that Alex never fixed that lousy windshield wiper of his," I continued, "that he was probably driving too fast in such a storm, and that he probably had had a couple of 'frosties' too many? Do you think it is God's will that there are no street lights along that stretch of road, and no guardrail separating that road and Boston Harbour?"

Nothing so infuriates me as the incapacity of seemingly intelligent people to get it through their heads that God doesn't go around this world with his finger on triggers, his fist around knives, his hands on steering wheels. God is against all unnatural deaths. And Christ spent an inordinate amount of time delivering people from paralysis, insanity, leprosy and muteness.

There are, of course, nature-caused deaths that are untimely and slow and pain-ridden and hard to understand. But violent deaths, such as the one Alex died - to understand those is a piece of cake. His younger brother, standing at the head of the casket at the Boston funeral, put it simply: "You blew it, buddy. You blew it."

The one thing that should never be said when someone dies is, "It is the will of God." Never do we know enough to say that.[10]

Unanswered Questions

Technology has to do with solving problems, and there is much technology in modern medicine. Theology very often has to do with living with problems, and there are many unanswered questions. We are not asked or able to solve all the problems, but we can contribute a great deal by allowing them to be shared.

The following is an anonymous poem which was pushed through the letter-box of a hospital chaplain's office:

Unanswered Questions

What is life? Where am I going?
In circles, wide unending circles
What is the solution?
Death, maybe
Life holds nothing for me,
But what does death hold?
Peace or unrest.
I'm unsure, uncertain,
But what of?
My ambitions or my fate?
What do I believe in?
Nothing.
There is no God,
No Christ, No Holy Ghost.
No-one can help me.
What do I do next?

A note at the bottom added: "These are my feelings, I hope they don't sound vindictive, but someone else must know of them."   It was important for the writer to express these thoughts even though they were not shared personally.

The carer must have the courage to say, 'I don't know', and must beware of platitudes and slick answers to difficult or unanswerable questions. A letter of thanks from a mother to the person who helped when her young son was dying reads, "Thank you for **not** telling me why David had to die." Sometimes the thinking expressed by Bishop John Taylor may be helpful (see next page).

"Some months ago I was asked by a friend to visit a young couple whose two-year old daughter had been found dead in her cot. They were stunned and haunted by the old question, Why? and, sometimes, Why her? I simply could not offer them the conventional reassurance about it all being in God's providence, a mystery now but one day to be seen as part of a loving plan. I know that many good souls derive lasting comfort from such counsel, and it certainly squares with a good deal in the Bible, and is to be found in many books of devotion and pastoral practice. But to me it has become unconvincing and suggests a picture of God I find impossible to love, arrogant though that sounds. I said to them instead that their child's death was a tragic accident, an unforeseeable failure in the functioning of the little body, that, so far from being willed or planned by God, it was for him a disaster and frustration of his will for life and fulfilment, just as it was for them, that God shared their pain and loss and was with them in it. I went on to say that God is not a potentate ordering this or that to happen, but that the world is full of chance and accident, and God has let it be so because that is the one sort of world in which freedom, development, responsibility and love could come into being, but that God was committed to this kind of world in love and to each person in it, and was with them in this tragedy, giving himself to them in fortitude, healing and faith to help them through. And their child was held in that same caring, suffering love."[11]

The Sharing of Suffering

Generally speaking, suffering has to be shared rather than explained. "I could see the pain in the doctor's face as he told me". The 'Why' questions are often both a cry for help ('Help me, I can't cope') and an expression of protest. To offer an intellectual explanation is clearly inappropriate in these circumstances. It is necessary, therefore, to move on to the 'How' and the 'What':

> 'How do we tackle this?'
> 'It's not what happens to you that matters, it's what you make of it.'

Such attitudes look at sickness, suffering and tragedy in terms of response, that is, what can be made of it. In another context Jesus said, "Gather up the pieces left over so nothing is wasted" (John 6.12). Every piece of life has potential value but often needs to be woven into the whole. All carers spend a great deal of time helping to pick up pieces and enabling people to use them creatively. We must not underestimate all the different elements, and the transforming power of human care.

All of us, carers and cared-for, are on a journey whose destination we understand only dimly:

> "We know we are searching for something, yet the nature of the thing we seek constantly eludes us. On this strange journey, in this tantalizing search, we often feel lonely and bemused, in need of guidance, encouragement, companionship. Not always knowing what we are asking, we reach out for the help of others."[12]

There is an important difference between 'companionship' and 'friendship'. 'Companion' literally means 'he who shares bread'. The companion can be objective because he offers care to someone who is not his friend. The companion can share the journey for a while, but when the time comes can go his own way. For the friend and the relative their involvement is such that they may find this too difficult. "My friends tell me that Spring is coming, when I am trying to let go of these things," said a dying patient when the visitors had left.

Faith and Doubt

Patients may not be able or wish to articulate their spiritual needs. Many have no formal faith, would not wish to have one, and appear to live and die successfully without one. Others have a faith which means a great deal to them. Their religion is an important part of their lives and from it they derive strength and inspiration, which sustains them in difficulties. Nonetheless, some practising Christians, including priests and members of religious orders, find it difficult to die and feel disappointment and guilt. It is possible that the manner of a person's dying has more to do with the fundamental ability to relinquish control than with whether he or she has 'real faith'.

Faith, like death, does not cancel out the basic way a person has functioned in life. The person who has not been able to let go in life will find it difficult to let go when dying. For example, a dominant wife of a clergyman who ran the parish and controlled everything around her tried unsuccessfully to control her own dying. This caused great difficulty not only for herself but to all who cared for her. Dying generally involves progressive relinquishment of control to others and a letting go into the unknown. Some who find this difficult may ask for euthanasia or pray for a speedy death as living with uncertainty is too terrifying. The problem for the carers is that we rarely know the true nature of an individual until 'the chips are down'. Dying is a last learning experience.

Some patients have a rudimentary faith from childhood.
This often gives rise to great uncertainty and, because their
God is a caricature, creates more problems than it solves. In
the time which remains it may be that such people have to be
supported by the faith of others. For many, faith and doubt
exist side by side in tension:

> "Doubt is not an enemy to be overcome. It is a friend
> with whom we need to live, a friend who gives to our
> faith the enrichment necessary for its growth, but who
> asserts his own rights in the house and can be a
> nuisance or even an agony." [13]

In short, doubt is faith in evolution.

Respect for the Other's Beliefs

The carer brings her own strengths, weaknesses, beliefs and
problems, but these must not be allowed to intrude and
impose a belief system on the patient.[14] We meet the patient
where he is and not where we happen to be; the patient is to
be accepted, respected, listened to and allowed to set the
agenda. Patients are often very weak and vulnerable and
must be protected from those who would seek to convert the
dying before it is too late.

There is an increasing number of patients who are adherents
of a non-Christian faith. When helping those of another
faith, one must be aware of and sensitive to their needs, try
to understand their problems, and take seriously their religious
tradition with its riches and resources.[15-19]

Faith

Faith is often thought of as an object or a possession: [20]

> 'He is upholding the faith.'
> 'I could never have got through without my faith.'

Yet a careful reading of the Gospel narratives would suggest that the following capture better the essential meaning of the word:

> 'a persistent reaching out' [20]
> 'a reaching out to what is beyond'
> 'an empty hand held out to God.'

It is important to recall that the one to whom Jesus said, "Truly I tell you today you will be with me in Paradise" (Luke 23.43), knew neither the Lord's Prayer (probably) nor the Apostle's Creed (certainly), nor had he been received by baptism into Church membership. The death bed is not a place for dogma and for preaching, it is a place for stressing:

- the unconditional love of God for the whole creation
- the forgiveness of God for past wrongs and shortcomings
- the promise of God that the best is still to come in that death is the gateway to fullness of life.

As one hospital chaplain said, ministering to patients had:

- made him redefine evangelism
- made him redefine the meaning of the Church
- given him a confidence to be with dying people
- given him a confidence that they would come to fullness in God
- made him appreciate that it is not necessary to get the traditional Christian message across and obtain a traditional response

- led him to offer the simple but profound message of God's unconditional love
- led him to believe that the realization of this in a person's life is a conversion experience.[21]

Accepting 'a reaching out to what is beyond' as a working definition of faith and 'the realization in a person's life of God's unconditional love for his creation' as an adequate description of a conversion experience is not easy for those brought up within a mainstream Christian denomination. This, however, is the recurring dilemma of the 'insider' *vis-à-vis* the 'outsider'.[20]

All too often, the 'insider' over-simplifies and attempts to contain his faith (and God) within fairly clearly defined boundaries. The result is a travesty of the truth even though it may fulfil the idolatrous need of the 'insider' for certitude. If there is one thing denied the Christian believer, it is certitude.[20] Christ says to those who follow him:

> "To you the secret of the Kingdom of God has been given." (Mark 4.11)

But it is still a secret, that is, a mystery. If it were self-evident, we would walk not by faith but by sight. The whole of the New Testament emphasizes that the reverse is true:

> "Faith is our guide, not sight." (2 Cor.5.7)

The challenge to Christians in terminal care is, mainly by life and partly by word, "to proclaim the year of the Lord's favour" (Luke 4.19).

> "If we have listening ears, God speaks to us in our own language, whatever that language may be."[22]

Hope

Hope has already been referred to (chapters 1 and 10).
Theological hope transcends all identifiable goals, and affirms
a worthwhile future in spite of the present circumstances.
Hope is at its starkest when we have been brought to nothing,
when there is no further move to make and nothing more can
be done. It is commitment to an unknown future which we
cannot imagine, much less bring about:

"The fig tree has no buds,
the vines bear no harvest,
the olive crop fails,
the orchards yield no food,
the fold is bereft of its flock,
and there are no cattle in the stalls.
Even so I shall exult in the Lord
and rejoice in the God who saves me."
(Hab.3.17-18)

This hope is a God-centred, God-given virtue and is a
product of faith.

"Faith will vanish into sight,
Hope be emptied in delight,
Love in heaven will shine more bright,
Therefore give us love."[23]

Love

The importance of love is well described in *'The Velveteen
Rabbit'*, in which a conversation is recorded in the nursery
between two toy animals, a velveteen rabbit and a skin
horse.[24] The rabbit is feeling neglected and unloved as
children's toys often are. The skin horse had lived longer in
the nursery than any of the other toys. He was so old that his
brown coat was bald in patches and showed the seams

underneath. He was wise, for he had seen a long succession of mechanical toys arrive to boast and swagger and, in due course, break their main springs and pass away. He knew that they were only toys and would never turn into anything else:

" 'What is REAL?' asked the rabbit one day, when they were lying side by side near the nursery fender. 'Does it mean having things that buzz inside you and a stick-out handle?'

'Real isn't how you are made', said the skin horse, 'It is a thing that happens to you. When a child loves you for a long, long time, not just to play with, but REALLY loves you, then you become Real.'
'Does it hurt?' asked the rabbit.
'Sometimes', said the skin horse, for he was always truthful. 'When you are Real you don't mind being hurt.'

'Does it happen all at once, like being wound up', he asked, 'or bit by bit?'
'It doesn't happen all at once', said the skin horse, 'You become. It takes a long time. That's why it doesn't happen to people who break easily, or have sharp edges, or who have to be carefully kept. *Generally, by the time you are Real, most of your hair has been loved off, and your eyes drop out and you get loose in the joints and very shabby. But these things don't matter at all, because once you are Real you can't be ugly, except to people who don't understand'*.

'I suppose **you** are Real', said the rabbit... the skin horse only smiled, 'The Boy's Uncle made me Real', he said 'That was a great many years ago, but once you are Real you can't become unreal again. It lasts for always!' "

The italicized section emphasizes the ultimate importance of **being** rather than **doing**. This is particularly relevant as the ravages of disease bring an increasing list of losses and limitations, and as weakness increases in the weeks or months before death. Despite everything, the individual must be valued for what she is and what she can still become.

Religious Care for the Christian

Each of the Christian traditions (e.g. Roman Catholic, Orthodox, Free Church) will use its own particular prayers and rituals to express the special relationship of grace there is between God and the sick person. The following comes mainly from the Anglican tradition.

Whereas spiritual care may be offered by any member of the caring team, religious care is the specific remit of the chaplain. Although the sacraments are a corporate act of the Church, religious ministry is personal to each individual. There are no simple answers and no official forms to be handed over the counter. In an increasingly computerized and impersonal society, any caring ministry should, principally through attitudes and actions, convey the message:

> 'The very hairs of your head are numbered by him in whose safekeeping you are held. The Creator of the world loves you with an infinite love. Whatever else, you matter to God, and you matter because you are you.'

What follows is not intended to be prescriptive but describes some approaches which have proved helpful.

The Bible

Religious care for the Christian is likely to include readings from the Bible. Indeed, many who had an active link with a church in the past but have had no recent association are glad to be reminded of once-familiar passages in the Bible or to be pointed to helpful verses. The Gideons International provide an invaluable service in making the Bible or the New Testament available in hospitals and hospices. These include a list of suggested passages for reading in different personal circumstances.

The Book of Psalms includes much which is particularly relevant to those who are ill, distressed or dying. For example, psalms 77 and 88 speak of the sense of abandonment by God which many experience. Others speak more positively of companionship and care (psalm 23); guidance (psalm 27); assurance (psalm 46); hope (psalm 121); openness before God (psalm 136); God's presence (psalm 139).

People may be helped by being reminded of Jesus' own fear and anguish as he faced his coming death (Mark 14.32-36), and of his final message to his disciples before his crucifixion (John 14-16). This begins with the familiar words:

"Set your troubled hearts at rest.
Trust in God always; trust also in me.
There are many dwelling-places in my Father's house;
if it were not so I should have told you." (John 14.1-2)

Romans 8.18-39 speaks of life in the Spirit. Verse 26 may be particularly helpful to those who, because of physical weakness or psychological distress, find verbal praying difficult or impossible:

"In the same way the Spirit comes to the aid of our weakness. We do not even know how we ought to pray, but through our inarticulate groans the Spirit himself is pleading for us." (Rom.6.26)

1 Corinthians 13 is again a familiar passage and one which emphasizes that love will never come to an end. These suggestions, of course, will not be appropriate for everyone or every time. There are no set texts. As always, it is necessary to be sensitive to individual need.

Prayer

Praying with a person should be short and to the point because people who are ill have a reduced attention-span. It is important that the person should be in a comfortable position and as relaxed as possible. If extemporary prayer is used it is important to centre it in the patient's concerns, doubts, beliefs and mood, i.e. encapsulate in a prayer what has been expressed by the patient in conversation - however irreverent or unorthodox this may seem:

"God, we offer John into your care, remembering his life and what he has achieved, and the lives which he has touched. We also acknowledge the pain, and the unfairness of what has happened. As we offer you what we don't understand, and our anger and despair, we ask that you will help John to make sense of what is happening to him in your time and in your way."

"God, we offer you the angry and hurt feelings which we have just shared. You who ask us to be honest in our dealings with one another and with you, help us to find your truth in the reality of our anger and hurt, remembering that, in your Son, you shared with us a common humanity."

Evening and Compline prayers can be readily adapted for use with those close to death. The Lord's Prayer is familiar to most people and sometimes provides all that is needed. Other suitable prayers include:

> "Defend, O Lord, this your servant with your heavenly grace, that he/she may continue yours for ever, and daily increase in your Holy Spirit more and more, until he/she come to your everlasting Kingdom."

This prayer not only asks for protection but also gives a sense of moving forward into abiding life and growth.

In recent years *'Footprints'*, by an unknown author, has become well known and is helpful to those who feel, like Jesus on the cross, that God has left them in their hour of need.

An informal laying on of hands with prayer is often appropriate. It can be done without any fuss, on either the head or a hand. This is a religious use of touch:

> "The grace of the Lord Jesus Christ flow forth upon you, and the blessing of God Almighty, etc."

The comments of two patients demonstrate the potential benefit of this form of ministry:

> "I am deeply grateful for the laying on of hands. I was aware of something which the Holy Spirit has been working out deep down inside me - sometimes very painfully - for a long time, and for which this seemed to be a culminating act of love and grace. I am very full of thankfulness to God."

> "Immediately I felt 'linked in' to that great universal body - Christ's Church - and became aware of the presence of God."

"I remember a girl of about 17 who was dying of cancer, a cancer in one shoulder which was like a rugby ball... She had a bad family background. Mother and father were at loggerheads with each other, her boy friend walked out on her, she was alone, she was abandoned. She said she had prayed and prayed and she felt that God did not listen to her. So I said to her, 'Well, say it, then: tell him he's abandoned you'. Eventually she did. Then I said to her, 'Now you're with Christ on the cross: that's what he said', and she suddenly got the message. She got it a bit queerly and I am not sure whether the theologians present would agree with her final summation which was, 'I see what I must do now; I must forget God and be with Christ.' But it was not the time for theological disputation. The idea was there and the completeness of the situation was there. She changed from that time."[25]

Prayer tends to be more difficult when we are sick or weak. Some who have been faithful in prayer throughout their lives find this hard to accept, and it may be that permission has to be given **not** to pray. A small cross or crucifix to hold is often helpful. Just as we have to hand over the care of our physical needs to others, so too we may have to leave the work of prayer to others. Prayer groups and Religious Communities are helpful in this respect but should be approached only with the patient's permission. Generally speaking, it is unnecessary to go into clinical detail. This may intrude on the patient's need for privacy and, in any case, "Your Father knows what your needs are before you ask him" (Matt.6.8).

Prayer, care and action often go together. The four friends in the gospel story went to the trouble of carrying the paralysed man to Jesus and dug out the roof to let him down to Jesus's feet (Mark 2.1-12). They did not **say** anything. Similarly the care and action of the carers at the bedside and the manner of their caring is part of the prayer. Sometimes it is a matter of, "Don't just sit there, **do** something"; at other times it is a matter of "Don't just do something, **sit** there" - and surround the sick person with love and prayer.

Prayer after death

The ancient prayer of commendation can be very helpful to the relatives and the carers as leave is taken and goodbyes made:

> "Go forward, O Christian soul out of this world,
> In the name of God the Almighty Father who made you,
> In the name of Jesus Christ who redeemed you,
> In the name of God the Holy Spirit who sanctifies you.
> May your guardian angel succour and defend you,
> May the Saints of God pray for you,
> May your portion be peace,
> And your rest today in Paradise."

The Sacraments

Baptism

Primarily a sacrament of initiation, baptism is also a sacrament of healing. Baptism represents incorporation into the Risen Christ, by which a person passes from death to life (John 5.24 and 1 John 3.14). This speaks of relationship and right-relatedness and is therefore a healing process. Maternity units teach the importance of physical bonding of the mother with her baby. In Baptism we have a spiritual bonding into Christ. The grace of the sacrament reaches down into the innermost being of the person (however small) and overflows into the whole situation and all involved, whether relative or carer, because 'no man (including no baby) is an island.'

Holy Communion

This is usually taken to the sick person from a service in church or hospital chapel, and can be powerfully therapeutic. For example, someone badly injured in a road accident wrote after discharge from hospital:

> "When you've been bashed you get a bit self-centred. You even wonder the point of praying 'Defend us in the same by thy mighty power; and grant that this day we fall into no sin, neither run into any kind of danger' - as if the prayer of the Church were designed to keep us in cotton wool. Holy Communion put me firmly back into the whole context of God's work in the world, and I began to feel the ground under my feet."

Anointing with Oil

Suggested forms of words for use with this ministry with the terminally ill and dying are given on the opposite page. Anointing may enable a dying person to let go of life. It may

[Name], I anoint you with oil, in the name of the Father, the Son, and the Holy Spirit, that the God of peace and love may be with you now and for ever."

"Outwardly and with sacramental oil your body has received anointing. So may Almighty God our Father inwardly anoint your soul, to strengthen you with all the comfort and the joy of His most Holy Spirit. Through the power of Jesus Christ our Lord may you be loosed from all that troubles you in body, mind or spirit; to praise the Blessed Trinity, one God, beyond all time and space eternally."

From *Pastoral Care of the Sick*: [26]

[Forehead]
"Through this holy anointing may the Lord in his love and mercy help you with the grace of his Holy Spirit."

[Hands]
"May the Lord who frees you from sin, save you and raise you up."

"Father in heaven, through the holy anointing grant [Name] comfort in his/ her suffering.
When he is afraid, give him courage;
when afflicted, give him patience,
when dejected, give him hope;
and when he is alone [or feels lonely] reassure him of the support of your holy people.
We ask this through Christ our Lord."

also help the relatives to let go of their loved one, particularly when they are finding this difficult. Anointing may thus bring peace not only to the dying person, but also to the family. A daughter, who found the dying of her father very difficult, wrote afterwards:

> "I had always been afraid of death, but in the end I found his peace a very beautiful thing".

Anointing will usually include an act of penitence (confession) and absolution. This may follow on from what has been shared privately with the priest in a counselling relationship. Forgiveness and reconciliation within the sick person, with others or with God can transform dying and death into a healing event as distress and anxiety are alleviated and broken relationships restored.

Life after Death

Letting go, but into what? Clergy in particular are asked about life after death: 'Are we just snuffed out, or is there something after death?' Questions such as 'What about the people I don't want to meet?' may be asked by those who have had great personal unhappiness. Some may decide they do not believe that there is a future life. It may be possible, therefore, to contemplate our own final extinction at death, or even desire it but, when it is a question of the death of someone we love, it is different. Love by its very nature must go on loving, and longs for a life of permanent uninterrupted union with the loved one.

It is God's love which gives us hope of life after death:

> "For I am convinced that there is nothing in death or life, in the realm of spirits or superhuman powers, in the world as it is or the world as it shall be, in the forces of the universe in heights or depths - nothing in all

creation that can separate us from the love of God in Christ Jesus our Lord." (Rom.8.38-39)

What this life will be like we do not know; the Bible is not specific. Because the chief hunger of our hearts is to love and to be loved, we must think of life beyond death in such terms. All our hopes, longings and deep desires will be fulfilled in ways more splendid than we can begin to imagine:

"We are told that eye cannot see nor ear hear, nor heart or mind conceive the joy of eternal life; the nearest we can get to it is to think of it as all the joys of loving and being loved, multiplied to infinity and brought to fulfilment, without separation and for ever."[27]

References

1   Zorza R, Zorza V. *A Way to Die.* Andre Deutsch, London 1980.
2   Brown A. Do you speak any Russian? *Contact* 1991; **8** (1): 2.
3   Vanier J. *The Broken Body.* Darton, Longman and Todd, London 1988.
4   Bloom A. Suffering. *Hospital Chaplain's Magazine* 1965; **1** (1).
5   Saunders C. 'Watch with me.' *Nursing Times* 1965; **61**: 1615-1617.
6   Wolff P. *May I hate God?* Paulist Press, New York 1979.
7   Campbell AV. *The Gospel of Anger.* SPCK, London 1986.
8   Dawson B. Forgiveness. In: Saunders C (ed). *St. Christopher's in Celebration: 21 years at Britain's first modern hospice.* Hodder & Stoughton, London 1988, p 110.
9   Tennyson A. 'The Village Wife'. *The Works of Alfred Lord Tennyson.* Macmillan, London 1896, p 514.
10 Coffin W. My son beat me to the grave. *Thanatos* 1989; Spring: 20-21.
11 Taylor JV. *Weep not for me.* World Council of Churches, Geneva 1985, p 11-12.
12 Campbell AV. *Rediscovering Pastoral Care.* Darton, Longman & Todd, London 1981, p 82.

13 Williams HA. *Tensions*. Mitchell Beazley, London 1976, p 45.
14 Mauritzen J. Pastoral care for the dying and bereaved. *Death Studies* 1988; **12**: 111-122.
15 Lothian Community Relations Council. *Religions and Cultures: A Guide to Patients' Beliefs and Customs for Health Service Staff*. Lothian Community Relations Council, Scotland 1978.
16 Speck P. *Loss and Grief in Medicine*. Baillière Tindall, London 1978, chapters 7-9.
17 Church Information Office. *Our Ministry and Other Faiths*. CIO, London 1983.
18 Greenacre R. *World Religions and Medicine*. Institute of Religion and Medicine, London 1983.
19 Neuberger J. *Caring for Dying People of Different Faiths*. The Lisa Sainsbury Foundation, London 1987.
20 Burdon C. *Stumbling on God*. SPCK, London 1990.
21 Woodroffe I. *Towards a Hospice Theology*. St George's House, Windsor 1989.
22 Attenborough R. *Words of Ghandi*. Wildwood House, London 1982, p 74.
23 Wordsworth C. (1807-1885). 'Gracious Spirit, Holy Ghost'. *English Hymnal* 1911, No. 396.
24 Williams M. *The Velveteen Rabbit*. Heinemann, London 1922.
25 Marteau L. Good news and bad news 2. In: Mclinsky MAH (ed). *Religion and Medicine*. SCM Press, London 1970, p 107.
26 International Commission on English in the Liturgy. *Pastoral Care of the Sick*. Catholic Book Publishing, New York 1983, pp 145-146.
27 Bishop H. *The Easter Drama*. Hodder & Stoughton, London 1958, p 59.

12   CARE FOR THE PROFESSIONAL CARERS

It is a sad observation that hospices have not always demonstrated the same care and compassion towards carers which won them public acclaim in the care of patients and families. Concern for the staff is a primary responsibility of councils of management and their National Health Service equivalents. Along with the Church generally, there is an urgent need for council members and senior staff to comprehend the liberating role of good management practice, and to follow the Biblical injunction to look after the needs of workers (1 Tim, 5. 17-18).

The stresses and rewards of caring for dying people are considerable and inextricably linked. Terminal care, however, is not the preserve of 'special' carers, rather it is ordinary people doing work in a particularly stressful setting. Other settings also generate high levels of stress and a parallel need for staff support (e.g. intensive care units, working with people with learning difficulties, and prisons).[1,2] Stresses that are more specific to hospice work are shown in Table 1.

Unless due consideration is given to the professional and personal needs of hospice staff, a variety of consequences may follow, including: [1]

- staff conflict
- hostility towards team leader
- deterioration in standards of care
- marital and family problems

- rapid staff turnover
- high sickness rate
- depression (chronic fatigue and lack of interest in life)
- mental disturbance
- 'burnout'.

Table 1   Sources of stress in the hospice setting

Difficulty in accepting the fact that the patient's physical and psychosocial problems cannot always be controlled

Frustration at being involved with a patient's family only after their emotional resources have been drained by the illness

Disappointment if expectations for patients to die a 'good death' (however this may be defined) are not met

Frustration at having invested large amounts of energy in caring for people who then die, taking this investment with them

Anger at being subjected to higher-than-standard performance expectations in prototypal facilities exposed to considerable scrutiny and publicity

Difficulty in deciding where to draw limits on involvement with patients and their families, particularly during off-duty hours

Difficulty in establishing a sense of realistic limitations on what the hospice service, which is expected to be all-encompassing, can provide

---

From Vachon 1979 [3]

Burnout describes the state in which the carer is no longer able to respond to the psychological needs of others in any depth, and is functioning increasingly in an 'automated' way. Objectivity has been abandoned, emotional resources have been drained, and the carer is surviving as best he can.[4]

Understanding One's Own Feelings and Experiences

Unresolved personal issues relating to loss and bereavement may be reactivated by working with dying patients and their families. Further, the emotional responses experienced by the dying are observed also in the carers. This needs to be acknowledged and provision made to deal with the issues raised.

Two responses to the needs of others are frequently encountered. One leads to over-involvement; the other to withdrawal. The Judaeo-Christian tradition can be interpreted so as to emphasize altruism to the detriment of one's own needs.[5] Denial is not just something employed by patients and relatives. Sometimes it is essential for a person's health, while at other times to deny distress is to deny oneself. Carers need permission to feel distressed, although this may not necessarily be at the time of crisis, when the most pressing need may be to keep going. Such feelings, however, if suppressed and unacknowledged, will lead in time to emotional exhaustion and/or physical illness.

A comment to a hospice doctor, "I suppose you become hardened to it in time and develop a protective shell" produced an emphatic "No!". Obviously, with experience, hospice staff become more familiar with the many practical challenges of terminal illness, and acquire a certain confidence. This is not, however, the same as becoming hardened. For many the opposite is true, and they feel more vulnerable as each year passes. Terminal care is, and always will be, emotionally demanding on those who care:

"It is hard to tell a patient 'Yes, it is cancer' or 'Yes, the illness seems to be winning'. It is particularly hard if the patient is 16 or 26, although even at 76 or 86 it is not easy. Indeed it may be suggested that, if ever it does become easy, a doctor may be sure that he is no longer of much use to his patients."[6]

Accepting One's Own Need for Support and Care

If the personal needs of carers are not identified and assimilated into professional practice, the effect may be the development of a *'persona'* or mask which conveys the spoken or unspoken message that 'It does not touch me'. It may also lead to behaviour which is anxiety-relieving in the short term (e.g. excessive smoking, eating, alcohol or sex) and to constant complaining. Others may cope with their anxiety by keeping at the margins of real involvement (and possibly complain about never being involved), because they find the weight of human distress too heavy to handle. No carer is immune from the very strong temptation to deny:

- the awfulness of what is happening
- the distress and confusion which is felt
- the sense of personal inadequacy which is often experienced when someone is dying.

The other extreme is to become over-involved, so that the whole of one's life revolves without boundaries round the care of needy people. The inability to set limits to one's involvement and therefore to resist being driven by the incessant needs of others can lead all too quickly to trouble.

Over-involvement may stem from an uncompromising idealism which drives the person to measure up to unrealistically high standards. It can be fired by ambition (either conscious or unconscious) or fear of failure. Alternatively, it may represent a desperate need to be loved in return for devoted care. Over-involvement may attract praise and gratitude, and has placed many talented individuals upon a pedestal, isolating them from colleagues and their own humanity. There is a subtle form of pride which seeks to convince carers that:

- they alone can meet the patient's needs
- the burden of the world's suffering rests upon their shoulders
- their resources are inexhaustible.

Carers who are so caught up in the need to help others will inevitably suffer in their personal and family life, and paradoxically may fail to meet appropriately the needs and demands of their patients. In addition, potential helpers can be 'de-skilled' and deterred by the apparent competence and self-sufficiency which is portrayed. Indeed, the picture of the person who exists only to serve is an oppressive one. An excessively competent person is also difficult to succeed because none will feel able to live up to such a standard.

The Gospel narratives indicate that the ministry of Jesus involved both giving and receiving. He is portrayed as busy and active, taking initiatives, teaching, healing and serving. But he also withdrew to be quiet and to rest, and insisted that his disciples do the same (Mark 6.31). At times, he was hungry, thirsty and tired, and had to come to terms with the limitations of being human.

The 'Good Enough' Carer

Just as it has been found necessary in parenting, the idea of the perfect carer needs to be replaced by that of a 'good enough' one.[7] One of the difficulties when caring for the dying is to know when one has done a good job. Setting team goals is vital for staff. Only by so doing can success or failure be measured, and individual carers be supported by a corporate perspective.

In a situation where the goals of recovery and cure are seldom appropriate, it is important to accept the reality of other goals. Even when no physical improvement is possible, there is still potential for healing in the psychological, social and spiritual dimensions.

The disciplined practice of:

- agreeing and recording goals
- reviewing them in the light of changing circumstances
- evaluating outcome after the patient's discharge or death

helps to avoid dangerous (and very seductive) dependency on compliments and flattery from patients and families, or members of staff. Yet genuine praise and encouragement within the broader context of constructive feedback affirms good practice and strengthens the recipient. They tend, however, to be sparingly given and poorly received. Why this is so is not immediately apparent.[8]

Motivation

It must be stressed that mixed motivation does not invalidate the quality of care, but that some understanding of why people become involved with dying patients and their families will contribute to sound care and appropriate job satisfaction.[9] People are drawn to hospice work from all walks of life and their motives are as varied as humanity itself. Human motives are never wholly altruistic. This is also true for those who see hospice work as a form of Christian service. 'We are doing this for the Lord' does not exempt them from the challenge and discipline of professional audit and appraisal.

The rewards carers seek from their work will reflect their motivation and expectations. It is therefore important to explore this area when a person is interviewed for a post.

Finding meaning in what one sees, witnessing a healing element in the face of seeming tragedy, discovering that a tiny light flickers in the blackest night, and experiencing the comradeship of good teamwork are among the rewards of hospice work. They shed light on why certain people count it a privilege to stay alongside the dying despite the demands it makes. Even so, it is necessary to develop strategies for supporting the carers.

Strategies for Coping

The individual personalities of the carers will be reflected in the care they seek. Hospice workers who opt out of some of the available support systems should not necessarily be considered to have refused help. They may well receive adequate support and care away from work. Some carers elect to use formal groups and 'debriefing' sessions, whereas others may be naturally more private and prefer to talk with individual colleagues, family and friends, or someone like a staff counsellor or chaplain on a one-to-one basis.[10] The tendency to standardize care (something the hospice movement has claimed to challenge) can subtly be reimposed without thinking.

Support Groups

Some people work naturally and effectively in a group, while others find individual 'space' for themselves essential. Support groups and time for oneself share the same objective, namely:

● providing a place where feelings may be expressed
● time for reflection
● a chance to grow through the problems and face a new challenge.

The group meeting offers time for mutual care and support when carers can learn and grow, particularly in the light of mistakes. Feelings of isolation are reduced, particularly for those working in the community, and humour together with the mixture of personalities helps to restore balance and a sense of proportion. Extensive research has been carried out on the expression of feelings in grief.[11,12] Less attention has been given to the different ways in which people may express anger (see also chapter 14; chapter 15, p 236-7). It would be helpful if future research could explore practical ways of discharging anger (one's own and the projected feelings of others) for the betterment of the health of professional carers.

The Mutual Nature of Support

It is regrettable that giving help is generally awarded higher status than receiving help. However, carers who can acknowledge their own need for support and receive it graciously set an important precedent, and may help eventually to modify present attitudes.

> A general practitioner attended the funeral of a boy who had been one of his patients. He found it very distressing and cried openly. He was comforted by the dead boy's grandmother who in turn was comforted by the doctor's visible distress - a sign that he cared.

The ability to listen to others in distress is partly linked to how well the carer feels that he or she has been listened to in the past. Frequently it is a patient or family member, intuitively aware of the need of the carer, who offers support and encouragement. The giving and receiving of support is a human activity and not the sole property of any one group.

Patients and their loved ones and professional carers are bound together as they experience the same situation from different perspectives. There is tenderness in mutual care.[13]

The Role of Management

Responsibility for providing support and making use of the help on offer rests equally with manager and carer.[14] Appreciation of the stresses of the work and enthusiasm for the team's goals are vital in building trust between carers and manager. Time must be allocated to listen to the team, to monitor morale and discuss stresses such as staff changes, inadequate resources and conflicts between team members. These practical matters, if neglected, may take on a disproportionate significance.

Mistakes (e.g. drug errors) should be handled with care because they are frequently as much a sign of failed management as of individual carelessness, and may reflect a particularly demanding or distressing situation on the ward. Errors are learning opportunities. For example, out of a particularly painful experience, a manager may be able to draw together new procedures and ways of working. Hitherto, little provision has been made for the carer who becomes temporarily or permanently unsuited to hospice work through personal bereavement or tragedy. This is no less a crisis than if a physical education instructor breaks a leg.

Self-Help

Assuming responsibility for oneself is an important aspect of personal and professional maturity. It helps carers to recognize their inter-dependence and encourages them to take seriously their own needs and those of others.

Growing self-awareness and learning to handle one's emotions, particularly anger, frustration and despair, will cause one to look more deeply at life. Death forces a reassessment of one's values; spiritual issues take on a new significance. For many today such territory lies unexplored and may be forbidding. Opportunities should be provided where carers can discover truth for themselves without pressure, within a caring and relaxed environment. The chaplain can offer much support and encouragement to individual carers and team alike, but spiritual considerations must be placed on a broader canvas than that of organized religion. This aspect of a chaplain's role is one which has emerged largely from the stresses and strains of hospice work, and is not yet normally seen as a significant part of the work of the hospital chaplain.

Carers should try to build balance into their lives:

- matching stress with relaxation
  the clamour of unending demands with some time for
- oneself
- using hobbies and exercise to release tension and restore inner harmony.

This will require time management and good planning. Help in developing these skills is an appropriate topic for training programmes for hospice workers (Table 2).

It is all too easy to take the stresses of work and off-load them on the family. If aware of this danger, steps can be taken to begin to unwind before arriving home. It may be helpful to walk for 10 minutes in a park before facing the children with all their exuberance. Family members of hospice staff often complain that their needs come second. There is a subtle blackmail which insists that those in distress, particularly the dying, must take precedence. Those whose work is continuously among the dying must, however, preserve the division between their professional role and their life as a spouse, parent, friend and member of the wider community. It should be appreciated, however, that those who lead or give out much during working hours need to recharge their batteries and should not be expected to take a prominent part in local community and church affairs.

Table 2   Suggestions for a balanced life

Proper living & eating conditions
- space to be alone
- adequate heating
- a balanced diet

A regular day off each week with time:
- for spouse/partner/friends
- to be oneself (e.g. pottering, gardening, painting)
- for outings (e.g. theatre, museums, countryside)

Time for professional study
- journals and books
- study days and conferences
- research
- writing

Time for 'selfing'
- taking restful holidays away from work and home
- annual retreat to Conference House or Monastery

Self-assessment
- at least annually

Prayer support
- by friends
- local congregation
- religious communities

Professional Development

Palliative care encompasses many aspects of traditional nursing, medicine, social work, pastoral care, rehabilitation and creative arts. Carers will come to this work with professional qualifications and experience, but they will need to build on their skills to meet new challenges and to learn fresh techniques. Attending conferences and workshops appropriate to their needs is an important part of supporting carers and also provides an opportunity to receive peer support and encouragement professionally. Equally helpful are visits and exchanges between staff of different hospices, particularly for those who work as the only representative of their profession in the local hospice.

Team Outlook

Teamwork is an essential ingredient of comprehensive care of the dying and bereaved (see chapter 9). No one discipline encompasses all the knowledge and skill which may be required, and no individual carer has all the resources necessary. Not only does the recipient of care need the availability of the team, but carers need to share the burden of responsibility. Seeing oneself as a member of a team is an important protection against over-involvement, looking to oneself to meet every need and losing one's professional identity. Decisions regarding policy, setting limits and taking unpopular steps are easier to handle and more likely to be observed when they represent the team response, and not that of an individual.

The discipline of being a team member is in the carer's best interests, though at times it may seem irksome. To see one's professional role within the context of the team takes an awareness and a sensitivity which do not grow overnight. For instance, a chaplain may bring communion to a patient and assume he is helping busy staff by requesting no assistance, instead of recognizing the need of a carer with no formal religious affiliation to share in the symbolism of uniting physical care with spiritual nurture. Team members hold it in their power to 'think team' or act independently. The former requires unselfishness and a measure of humility, but it brings reward.

References

1 Vachon MLS. *Occupational Stress in the Care of the Critically Ill, the Dying and the Bereaved.* Hemisphere Publishers, Washington 1987.
2 Richards C. *The Health of Doctors.* King's Fund Publishing Office, London 1989.
3 Vachon MLS. Staff stress in care of the terminally ill. *Quality Review Bulletin* 1979; May: 13-17.
4 Cherniss C. *Staff Burnout: Job Stress in the Human Services.* Sage, London 1980
5 Ainsworth-Smith I, Speck P. *Letting Go: Care of the Dying & Bereaved.* SPCK, London 1982, chapter 7.
6 Twycross RG. *A Time to Die.* Christian Medical Fellowship Publications, London 1984.
7 Winnicott DW. *The Child, the Family and the Outside World.* Penguin, Harmondsworth 1964.
8 Bond M. Stress and self-awareness for nurses. Heinemann, London 1986.
9 Eadie H. Psychological health of clergymen. *Contact* 1973; **42**: 22-35.
10 Burroughs A. Hospice thoughts. *Nursing Times* May 1985.
11 Kubler-Ross E. *On Death and Dying.* Tavistock, London 1970.
12 Parkes CM. *Bereavement. Studies of Grief in Adult Life.* Pelican Books, London 1975.
13 Suttie I. *The Origins of Love and Hate.* Kegan Paul, London 1935, chapter 6.
14 Hertzberg F. *Work and the Nature of Man.* Staples Press, USA 1968.

SECTION IV : CONFLICT

13 PROMOTION OF HEALTHY COMMUNITY LIFE

People often say, "Being healthy is something I never noticed until I'd lost it". In practice that has been the basis for the National Health Service:

- solving the problems posed by illness
- restoring something lost
- restoring a more or less properly functioning body and (most people would add after reflection) mind.

But when you dig deeper into the idea of health, it begins to look different. What, for instance, is the good of simply operating on a child's diseased tonsils or treating a chronic bronchitic, knowing that each must return to a poverty-stricken, disease-ridden community? The operation needs doing and drugs keep the bronchitic going, but would it not be more sensible also to spend some money and effort on trying to improve the community's condition, and so help its members to stay healthy in the first place?

Some improvements in preventive care are being pursued, but it is generally agreed that there is still a long way to go. For some reason, preventing illness seems to be less appealing than curing it. It may be that 'not being ill' is less noticeable than being 'cured', and accordingly attracts less money. Anyhow, the basic question remains: what keeps people well?

Clean water, food, sanitation, etc. obviously help, but even if we had enough money to carry out a thoroughly effective public health programme of preventive measures, as well as continuing essential medical treatments, the evidence suggests that all would still not necessarily be well. Health seems in some way elusive. Our expectations of 'reasonable' functioning have risen higher and higher, until the expanding demand for ever more costly services begins to look suspiciously like a demand for something else - happiness perhaps?

But is it sensible to expect a State-run service to provide more than the minimum conditions for 'reasonable functioning'? In any case, what could that 'more' be? The apparently insatiable demand for counselling, support, and therapies of every kind suggests that the longed-for 'more' is something much less amenable to treatment, and much more to do with our personalities, with how we are and feel as people. How we are as people cannot be in isolation; it includes how we are with other people. But what can any government do about essential human nature, the way humans deal with each other?

Care in the Community?

Many people are coming to believe that the best answer is to encourage and promote care in the community. In general, community is a 'hurrah' word, standing for tolerance, support and caring. It is the way in which we are helped to love our neighbours as ourselves, and it is frequently and happily the case that many communities provide support and comfort, and nourish affection and courage. In such cases, the idea of care in the community seems both sensible and practical; carry out skilled and technologically complicated procedures in expensively equipped hospitals and then discharge the patient to the bosom of the family. Or at least to the bosom of local health care and the 'caring community', hoping that the community's nature will be such as to maintain morale and prevent the recurrence of illness. And of course such care also has the attraction of looking cheaper (though it may not be), and may sometimes be recommended on these financial grounds.

But there is a danger of misunderstanding. Communities vary: some are censorious, stifling and inquisitive. Families vary also. An eminent lecturer once caused annoyance by criticizing the family for its 'squalid secrets'. Although our families are for many a source of endless interest and happiness, they can also smother; witness the experience of Jesus after he began his public ministry:

> "When his family heard about it they set out to take charge of him. 'He is out of his mind', they said."
> (Mark 3.21)

Families can also be places of pain and isolation, where there is little communication or affection between parent and child, or among brother and sister.

Any policy therefore which takes the community seriously, needs also to have addressed the following questions:

- how big is the functioning community? Is it parliamentary constituency, town, local authority ward, village, shopping area, or just a few streets?
- on the evidence of its own inhabitants, in what ways does it function well and in what ways does it function badly?
- how can it be helped to function better?
- what do we mean by 'better'?

How big is the functioning community?

The answer depends on what function is being considered.[1] In the 1960s, when a branch of the Samaritans was started in Sheffield, it was found that the suicide rate was half the national average. No one knew why. Local pride in industry (steel, coal, heavy engineering) may have had something to do with it, along with the clannishness of Sheffielders who tended to stay put and have mum round the corner. Other factors affecting morale probably include:

- past history
- the success or failure of the local football team(s)
- the availability of jobs, good pop bands, 'country' and other music in local pubs
- interest groups and evening classes
- shops, parks, buses
- churches, hospitals, schools
- university, polytechnic, colleges of further education.

Much has been written about communities.[2,3] Effective caring requires, on the one hand, large-scale support from the local authority, the National Health Service and/or the Department of Social Security. On the other hand, for practical purposes, it needs an area much smaller than city size:

"A true community, of which the members are able to be in personal relationship with one another, cannot be very large. It is at least necessary that its members should be able to meet face to face, with fair frequency, over a period of time. Empirically, this seems to limit the size of true human communities to somewhere between 500 and 1000 people. When they get bigger than this, relationships between members begin to be depersonalized, and folk are seen not as persons but become categorized instrumentally as workers or consumers or taxpayers or whatever. And when this point is reached, such social groupings begin to damage their members' health instead of providing good soil in which health can grow. When communities grow too big, there is no longer a possibility of all the members being able to share their experience: so they split up into subgroups, each of which develops its own idiosyncratic idea of what it is to be healthy; and this fragmentation of norms contains the seed of misunderstanding and conflict. The effect of community size on health is grievously understudied in our mass-mad society; and, of course, we see the results of this neglect all around us. A truly healthy society can only be thought of as a community of communities."[1]

Five hundred to one thousand people is considerably less than a typical Church of England parish of 4,000-9,000 people; perhaps a small estate, a village or just two or three streets. The practical helping of those who are ill and of those who care for them depends very much on close proximity. Fifty yards may make the crucial difference between 'popping in' and having to 'go out' to see someone. But, in any case, illness often has an emotionally isolating effect on the carer.

Take, for example, a woman who looked after her severely disabled niece. She received little help except from people who lived nearby, and even that was restricted by her reticence:

" 'You see neighbours is good, and often, if I go out, I leave the key with them and they pop in and see to her.'
Interviewer: 'How often does this happen?'
'Only occasionally, you see I don't like putting on people'."[4]

Nearness is what matters; and it is to the physically near that most people feel at least some obligation.

How Well is the Community Functioning?

Communities function variably, and differently for different people. Many parish priests and ministers hear people lamenting the loss of the friendly cosy community of some over-crowded city district, contrasting unfavourably with the lonely expanses of a huge overspill housing estate or the isolated dwellings of a comfortable suburb. Mobility and known faces seem crucial, particularly to the elderly. Most of us know at first or second hand about the effect on local happiness of the closed-down school, post-office, surgery, church, pharmacy or corner-shop.

Without these local facilities people have to make major expeditions for quite ordinary daily needs (if they are physically able), and they are much less likely to meet *en route* people they recognize. Similarly, we know the importance of policemen, teachers, barmen, shopkeepers, postmistresses and milkmen. They are all familiar and therefore reassuring figures, and play a vital part in the intangible but priceless network of communal awareness.

Distance matters less if everyone has a car. The insulating effect of a car, however, means that people do not so easily meet or get to know each other; and being a known face is more or less essential for attracting help from 'the community'. It helps too to have a pleasant and undemanding personality and conscientious neighbours. But people's experience varies widely and the only way to find out what it is like for other people is to listen to them.

The hospice itself is an example of specialized functioning in community. Here patients and staff know each other's faces, accept each others' roles and share a common purpose. There are tensions among staff, among patients, between staff and patients, between staff and relatives, between patients and their families, and between the hospice and the local community. These tensions can be admitted, however, and worked through where possible, giving an overall feeling of acceptance. This is reassuring, and is one of the marks of a healthy community, whose members are aware of their own interdependence. There is also a hierarchy, partly carried over from the general hierarchical assumptions of the average hospital, and partly and properly the result of differing clinical responsibilities.

This need not, however, entail an authoritarian atmosphere. A good and regular staff meeting will enable members to express both happiness and distress, fears and hopes, resentment and appreciation. This is particularly important when there is a rapid succession of deaths, staff are over-worked and there is not enough time to get to know the patients and their families properly. At such times unhappiness will grow unless the danger is realized, and it cannot be realistic or fair simply to place the burden of responsibility on the medical director or matron. Both need, perhaps more than anyone else, the support of a definite structure which will give the community's interdependence real meaning.

Personalities also can damage the community but need not, provided the unthinkable can be both thought and said aloud in an atmosphere of openness and acceptance. Here again, the staff meeting is crucial, though dealing with conflict is something that many Christians find difficult. On the basis of a brief account of a meeting in Jerusalem in about AD49 (Acts 15), it is often felt that Christians ought to be of one mind and to be able to say, like those in Jerusalem, "It is the decision of the Holy Spirit, and our decision" (Acts 15.28). Thus, when disagreement erupts (as is inevitable in any discussion of importance) some Christians feel obliged to deny that their opponents are led by the same Spirit.

Here the hospice experience is illuminating because patients with a non-Christian faith, or none, not uncommonly show the qualities of honesty, courage, considerateness and love which, in Christian terms, are considered to be fruits of the Holy Spirit. To some this is obvious enough, but it conflicts with one strand of Christian teaching which tends to limit the work of the Spirit to the Church. Hospice experience opens one's eyes, and saves one from the habit of judging according to one's own unexamined assumptions. It forces one to recognize and delight in the generosity and wideness of God's giving. It also compels one to look for his gifts in those one disagrees with. The love of God does not demand that all must think alike.

How Can a Community be Helped to Work Better?

The more local the better. With home helps, surgeries, churches, shops, the nearer they are the more we can use and enjoy them. But they are seldom 'cost-effective'. A slimmer bus service produces a better-looking balance sheet, but a missed bus means waiting another hour for the next one. A large supermarket is useful if you have a car, but it is a long way to carry the potatoes since the corner shop closed down. It is not only politics that is the art of the possible. It would cost many millions of pounds to maintain and staff a church building in every small community. Consequently, church officials are forced to 're-organize', i.e. close down buildings and withdraw paid staff. Sometimes it is a blessing, and the local body of Christians for the first time begins to:

- discover lay ministry
- value fellow-Christians
- experience the possibilities of its members being actively the Body of Christ.

But this blessing nearly always comes because of financial pressures which no one would have chosen, and which involve the incalculable effects of closing buildings which have been consecrated to God. The same 'market' pressure operates in all other spheres. If we are to stop simply hoping for the best, hard financial decisions have to be made. For instance, should we:

- discontinue all transplants and spend the money on home helps and mental health care?
- stop hip replacements for the over-75s?
- double postage charges and so be able to keep loss-making sub-post offices open?
- tax motor transport heavily and reinvigorate public transport and railways?
- increase the community charge by 30% and have better libraries and clean streets?
- re-introduce the sale of pew spaces and keep the local Victorian church open?

Such extreme proposals, if ever they saw the light of day, would undoubtedly at once be ruled out as misguided, authoritarian, insensitive or impossible. But what then? Some decisions have to be made, and there seem to be only three possible courses:

- the **utopian option** with countless pots of gold at the rainbow's end providing the means to do all that we desire and feel that we deserve
- a **draconian axe-wielding budget** as caricatured above
- a **mixture** more or less as before.

But whichever of the three we adopt, there is still no guarantee that it would do the desired trick, and make us either healthy or happy. The desire for 'more', which keeps the needs of the National Health Service on every politician's indignation-list, goes much deeper than this or that improvement. Identifying, articulating, and meeting that desire at the depth it requires will be much more difficult because it will demand something **personal** from us all; something more than intelligence, money and hard work, desirable though all these things are. But also, unlike the utopian and the draconian, it may be both possible and constructive. For the attempt will force us (as the current 'we all deserve health' assumption does not) to consider people's deepest needs. And this includes listening to what they are saying.

What do we Mean by 'Better'?

We should no doubt be better off if we achieved the World Health Organization's goal of health as 'a state of complete physical, mental and social well-being'. But that is precisely the puzzle: what is well-being? Nonetheless, the World Health Organization has made it plain that, in the matter of being well or ill, more is involved than a diagnosable and treatable condition. Accordingly, we are compelled to consider what health and humanity are for and consequently the ways of God to human beings. This is no place for an elaborate doctrine of human nature and destiny, but some things are clear.

1. There is no blueprint for a healthy community in the Bible, or in anyone's brain, from which we can extract usable instructions. There is, instead, a process of discovery, interaction, delight and obedience called abundant life or *shalom* (see chapter 7).[5] We could also call it the Kingdom of God, the common life in the Body of Christ, or salvation. Those words do not **describe** what we are offered, they only point to the area in which unusual happinesses might happen, and sometimes do. They point to the Church. They do not imply, however, that the Church corporately and in its individual members need not be seriously involved in the everyday life of the community.   But here is the Church's *raison d'etre*.

2.   We need each other.   A psychiatrist once suggested that healing involved a 'restoration of the capacity to love'. He might have added, the capacity to receive and accept love. Love is a big word, and we may reasonably be shy of claiming it.   Fortunately, however, it includes listening, and that is something we can all recognize.   We all know, or at least hope for, the pleasure of being listened to.   It does not sound much, but it is relatively rare.   In most conversations we tend to listen only to a few salient points and wait more or less patiently for the speaker to finish so that we can get on with what we want to say.   This is a relatively civilized way of operating, but it is neither therapeutic nor loving. Christians are often bad listeners:

> "Many people are looking for an ear that will listen. They do not find it among Christians, because these Christians are talking when they should be listening. But he who can no longer listen to his brother will soon be no longer listening to God either; he will be doing nothing but prattle in the presence of God too... One who cannot listen long and patiently will presently be talking beside the point and be never really speaking to others, albeit he be not conscious of it. Anyone who thinks his time is too valuable to spend keeping quiet will eventually have no time for God and his brother, but only for himself and for his own follies."[6]

People long to be listened to.   But for how long?   The difficulty once again is that our needs are seemingly endless. The patient who is told that it is her doctor's day off feels let down.   Similarly, people in 'caring' or service jobs are often made to feel that theirs is no nine-to-five job, no mere contract, but a much more open-ended commitment of limitless self-giving.   Such open-endedness, if accepted, imposes an unbearable strain. It tempts the carer to use overwork as a proof of caring, makes the recipient over-dependent and, most importantly, is false to the nature of love, which is receiving as well as giving. It is here that the ideal and the real can meet constructively, and realistic self-giving becomes possible. For while I must listen to you and give what I can, you in your turn have a need to listen and give. One-way giving turns into condescension and patronage. This means that the apparent givers, the 'strong' (doctor, nurse, chaplain, teacher, administrator, policeman) must admit their own needs and weaknesses. Sharing is essential.

This is the truth behind the World Council of Churches' vision of a 'just, participatory, and sustainable society'. It applies to all human beings, inside and outside the Church, and between Church and community. It applies particularly to the Church's own life, which becomes a hypocritical nonsense if genuine love is missing, however dynamic and impressive it may otherwise appear. A large membership is encouraging, but does that kind of 'success' really sum up God's intention? William Temple remarked that the Church is the only co-operative society founded for the benefit of non-members, and we should surely leave the numbers game to God and stop worrying incessantly about recruiting members. We can certainly stop putting up posters saying "Jesus the carpenter needs joiners". Many people are non-joiners, but they are still aware of the need for love. Does the local church stand for this interdependence above all, or is it seen by our neighbours as just another group of enthusiasts, a club?

3. **We are each personally responsible.** St Paul says we are to carry each other's burdens. This is community life in action "and in this way you will fulfil the law of Christ" (Gal.6.2). St Paul also says "everyone has his own burden to bear" (Gal.6.5). This apparent contradiction is a recognition

of fact. The personal burden is the recurring need for a change of mind (*metanoia*), that is, turning from what is bad to the source of good, accepting the need of a Saviour. No other human being can do this for me, although my fellow Christians may powerfully kindle my affections and strengthen my desire to change. The matter of and responsibility for repentance is mine; I am alone before my Creator and Saviour. Further, repentance is not a 'one-off' event. It needs continual renewal and carries with it the call to be a faithful steward of all that God has given me. A great part of that stewardship is loving my neighbour as myself, recognizing that I depend on him/her as he/she depends on me.

4.   We are different.   Each person is unique. There is no earthly or heavenly reason why we should all think the same, or respond in the same way to God's leadings. Vigorous and healthy life, for example, in hospitals, the arts, industrial firms, local government, British Telecom, or the Body of Christ depends on:

- the flourishing of variety
- freedom for people to speak their minds and disagree, listen and question.

Conversely, one of the marks of a hard, unhealing, uncreative community is a rigid division between what is claimed to be 'orthodoxy' and 'dissent', between the accepted way of behaving and the suggestions of the 'awkward squad'. Which description fits our local church? How can we ensure also that, in our hospitals, hospices and homes, dying Sikhs or Muslims or Jews or unbelievers are, and feel they are, truly accepted? For they are not merely the passive recipients of Christian charity nor merely the raw material with which we are to work out and display our own discipleship, but God's creatures beloved by him, and as such to be respected and appreciated in their own right.

5. We depend on God. Bitter experience shows that none of these longed-for things will happen lastingly unless the exploration of truth and love is undertaken in the light of eternity, in the certainty that we are God's creatures with no prescriptive right to possess or circumscribe the "high and holy one who inhabits eternity" (Isa.57.15). In depending on God we are not simply receivers of his gifts, we are also in a 'covenant' relationship. He is our God and we are his people, and in obedience we have to keep our side of that covenant. This is not simply because obeying his commands to care for the sick, the destitute and the imprisoned, and to love each other is prudent social behaviour. Nor is it only because we want to be liked and valued, but because it is **God**'s will, what he wants. And he wants a great deal; he wants us as friends (John 15.14).

> "Want itself is a treasure in heaven... God wanted the communication of his divine essence, and persons to enjoy it. He wanted worlds, he wanted spectators, he wanted joys, he wanted treasures... It is incredible, yet very plain. Want is the fountain of all his fullness. Want in God is treasure to us." [7]

We could put it differently. We could say with the Westminster Confession that our chief end is "to glorify God and enjoy him for ever" or agree with Ruskin that one of the chief objects of education is to make us capable of honesty and delight. The point is that the financial, technical, and spiritual needs of the sick leave us unsatisfied and uneasy because our efforts to meet their needs, whether apparently successful or not, make it clear that those needs are in the end more than any human being can supply. And what is true for them comes to be seen in the end as true for the supposedly healthy. For the truth is that we all have been created not just for tolerable functioning, but for glory.

6. We are afraid of death. Here again, we vary. Often people profess to be afraid only of the process of dying. Perhaps they can express this fear because with luck the process will not last long, so that reassurance about it is possible. But others have a secret and often unadmitted fear of the loneliness and everlastingness of simply being dead. In the poem *'Before the Anaesthetic' or 'A Real Fright'*,[8] a patient lies in bed and hears church bells:

> "Swing up! and give me hope of life,
> Swing down! and plunge the surgeon's knife.
> I, breathing for a moment, see
> Death wing himself away from me
> And think, as on this bed I lie,
> Is it extinction when I die?
> I move my limbs and use my sight;
> Not yet, thank God, not yet the Night...
>
> Almighty Saviour, had I Faith
> There'd be no fight with kindly Death.
> Intolerably long and deep
> St Giles' bells swing on in sleep:
> 'But still you go from here alone'
> Say all the bells about the Throne."

The point does not need to be elaborated; it needs to be admitted and not concealed by whistling in the dark. For along with the admission of our varying natural fear of the wholly unknown, we put belief in a Saviour. Our belief is that we stand before him whether in earth or heaven, and are not parted, "Members, though distant, of one Head".[9] And, because we cannot know what life in Light is like, we are freed from the compulsion to suppose that this or that theory is all that can be said. Questions may well arise (what if it is not light, but dark?), but so does hope:[10]

"Dear, beauteous Death! the jewel of the Just,
        Shining nowhere, but in the dark;
What mysteries do lie beyond thy dust,
        Could man outlook that mark!

He that hath found some fledg'd bird's nest may know
        At first sight, if the bird be flown;
But what fair well or grove he sings in now,
        That is to him unknown."

7. We are part of God's creation. We live in our world, not merely on it, and our planet has a rhythm of birth and death, seedtime and harvest, coming to be and passing away. The eternal silence of infinite space may indeed in one sense be terrifying, but it does not belittle us, as we are part of it. Nature certainly is "red in tooth and claw",[11] but she 'shrieks' only against the limited and peculiar creed that God does not care about the fall of a sparrow, that he does not take pleasure in all that he has made, and that somehow living should not include dying.

Implications

The above seven points affect our budgeting, our praying and our planning. Home help, local and domiciliary services of all kinds appear to be more important **for the community's health** than dramatic interventions and sophisticated treatments. If we cannot have both, domiciliary help should not be the service to be whittled down. Local help is more sustainable.

The system should also be just, and justice does not stop at the English Channel or the Mediterranean. It is not possible, either emotionally or intellectually, for most of us to agonize about underpaid tea-plantation workers as we drink our tea.

Even so, injustice is still injustice, and we cannot be satisfied with it.

There is a vital part too for the Church, "both those who have confessed the faith and those whose faith is known to you alone".[12] Our expectations and beliefs about the Church are remarkably different, as any dispute reveals (e.g. women's ordination). But although our expectations vary so much, we all share the belief that the Church's life is sustained by God, not by our own choice and efforts.

The local church may be, often is, neither just nor participatory, but it is the church we have, and it is "the blessed company of all faithful people", the mystical Body of Christ. It represents and contains the supreme puzzle for any believer or seeker:

- the split between what should be and what is
- the failure of the grace-filled community
- the simultaneous existence of abundant life and resentful sin
- love almighty and ills unlimited
- the even now and the not yet.

The puzzle is sharpened by the obvious fact, disconcerting to some and encouraging to others, that God's grace is not confined to the Church, and can bring about marvellous results among any group of humans who are seeking the true and the good. That God is generous is surely good, but it can be undeniably disconcerting, as the labourers discovered in the vineyard in the heat of the day (Matt.20.1-15). Some Christians accordingly, when faced with God's apparent gifts of grace outside the Church, try to preserve the perceived pattern of salvation by arguing either that the apparent good is not really a true good (which is to call white black, and is described by Jesus himself as the sin against the Holy Spirit,

Mark 3.22-30) or that those on whom the good has been bestowed are 'really' Christian at heart, what have been called 'anonymous' Christians. But such ingenuity is unnecessary. God's gifts are not relative goods, like money, status, success or fast cars, which depend for their value on one person having more than another. They are simply good, to be received, delighted in, and **shared**, in Christ's ongoing work of healing.

One part of that work is comparatively straightforward. It needs a great deal of detailed local work to ensure that we are trying to meet needs which are there, not needs which are not. There are and can be no detailed blue-prints, but loving struggling Christians will certainly find ways of constructive neighbourliness.[13] This may involve starting and supporting local groups which may be formal, e.g. under the aegis of the local authorities, or informal and untidy with many loose ends. Abundant life is overflowing.

In either case, much careful thought needs to be given to sensible and efficient administration. Such work is not an alternative to love. As Archbishop Fisher pointed out, effective administrative action in this field **is** pastoral care. Further, enthusiasts need to remember that experience makes many people wary of collective activity because committees may be led into insensitive or ruthless actions which individual members would personally deprecate.

It is unfortunately true that 'the common good' may become oppressive, even an excuse for bullying people into what is deemed good for them. Hence the common criticisms which are levelled at 'do-gooders' and the 'nanny state'. The answer is not to cease doing good and abolish nannies, but to avoid the dangers by being aware of them.

Nonetheless this work will avoid turning into a bustling activism only if we listen to those who have known the healing power of a community in their own experience. For example, teamwork and trust are common in hospitals, hospices, house groups, family therapy, and group work of many kinds, including industrial and mining processes. In *'The Church as a Healing Community'*, the author remarks:

> "In my daily work in the therapeutic community I experience a depth of loving acceptance by colleagues and patients which is healing: this must be what love (*agape*) really means." [14]

He goes on to ask why he does not experience this kind of forgiving love in his local congregation. Some will echo his words, while others may have had a happier experience; but all will agree that our local church is imperfect. However, the Church is not a static institution, it is not merely the garrison of a fortress guarding some motionless inert deposit of truth for fear it may be damaged or lost. Rather, the Church is the body of Christ, and is alive; and to be alive is to change and be renewed. The early Christians knew that the Church is imperfect, and one of our reasons for trust in God's providential care of his people is paradoxically the plain speaking of the New Testament about those shortcomings, particularly in the letters of St Paul.

Nonetheless St Paul is also clear in his confidence that Christ not only gave himself for the Church, but lives in it and will make it glorious, without stain or wrinkle (Eph.5.27). Although the Church has far to go, the Kingdom of God is both among us now and yet to come. Our present business is not improvement or decoration but transformation, and it is certain that no group of people who really listen and tell the truth to each other with goodwill can possibly remain unchanged.

The other part of the work, and the more difficult, is being faithful to the crucial truth that we are not applying rules and hard-won experience to a set of problems. Abundant life, *shalom*, cannot be simply the end-product of our well-intentioned efforts. That will come only when all things are reconciled in Christ (Col.1.20). Our work is personal and individual, but is done in concert with others. Separately, it means that we find ourselves:

- checking the poisons cupboard
- sitting on committees
- planning palliative care
- puzzling over the budget
- grieving with the sad
- being delighted or dismayed by the unexpected.

But in the Spirit (1 Cor.2.9-10) we are also **together** exploring the deep things of God, "the unsearchable riches of Christ" (Eph.3.8).

References

1   Mathers J. Health in the Community. *Chrism* 1978; **21** (May 6): 9-16.
2   Seebohm. *Report of the Committee on Local Authority and Allied Personal Social Services*. Cmnd 3703. HMSO, London 1968.
3   Clark D. *Basic Communities: Towards an Alternative Society*. SPCK, London 1977.
4   Bayley MJ. *Mental Handicap and Community Care*. Routledge & Kegan Paul, London 1973, p 283.
5   Davies JG. *Worship and Mission*. SCM Press, London 1966, p 130.
6   Bonhoeffer D. *Life Together*. SCM Press, London 1954.
7   Traherne T. (1670) In: *Centuries of Meditation Book I, Sections 41 & 42*. Clarendon Press, Oxford 1960.
8   Betjeman J. *'Before the Anaesthetic' or 'A Real Fright'*. In: *Collected Poems*. John Murray, London 1958.
9   Baxter R. 'He wants not friends that hath thy love'. *English Hymnal*. Oxford University Press, Oxford 1906, No. 401.
10 Vaughan H. (1695) Friends departed. In: *Oxford Book of English Verse*. Oxford University Press, Oxford 1961, p 409.

11   Tennyson A. (1850) *In Memoriam*. Oxford University Press, Oxford 1946, stanza 55.
12   *Alternative Service Book*. SPCK, London 1980, p 102.
13   Lambourne RA. *Community, Church and Healing: A Study of the Corporate Aspects of the Church's Ministry to the Sick*. Longman & Todd, London 1963.
14   Martin D. *The Church as a Healing Community.*   Guild of Health, London 1958.

14   A CRY FROM THE HEART

At various stages throughout the deliberations of the working party, strong disagreement was expressed. This was often between those holding a more 'fundamentalist' view of the Bible and those holding a more 'liberal' view. After one heated exchange, one member of the Working Party wrote the following cri de coeur.

This Working Party is composed of polite members of the caring professions. Certain standards of cordiality are taken for granted. Meetings begin with a silence introduced by carefully chosen religious extracts. We are dealing with questions of life and death which have involved the religious and medical establishments for generations, and harnessed the emotions as well as the thoughts of many. Outside the quiet room in which we meet are violent ideological struggles and wars and persecutions concerning what is most sacred and most treasured in our existence. We are not detached from our historical roots. Can we anaesthetize the savagery? On the other hand, can we afford to leave aside the pain of conflict involved in our work, just to make ourselves comfortable?

Group Dynamics

In attending courses on group dynamics, I was given an insight into group behaviour. Roles are taken up, games played, patterns constituted, which may remain largely unconscious. It is my feeling that, in this group, little anger

216

gets expressed, and I find myself carrying the group shadow in this respect. I find the anger that gets into me does not always belong to me. The difficulty is that I am equally aware of my own personal agenda of problems which I can easily be led to project into the group. It is only a very exceptional prophet who does not need to heed the warning to look after the 'beam' in his own eye.

I wonder if we thought we could contain all that we are encountering or being invited to encounter in a straightforward text. Here is the dilemma. If we delve more deeply into the human condition, we shall probably not produce anything in print. If we do not, we shall at worst produce something so bland as to be discarded along with all the other unsolicited mail or, at best, something that coincides with the highest common factor of bearable reality in the group.

Fundamentalism Versus Universalism

In the confrontation between 'fundamentalism' and 'universalism' there are those whose predominant fear is that, if we do not bear witness to a literal reading of the Bible, we will betray our Lord. To these it may appear that anyone presenting a different attitude is not really a Christian. On the other hand, if you look at the Bible or any source book of revelation with a mind conditioned by the fears and prejudices of centuries, you do not do justice to the mercy of Christ or the universal appeal intended by him. And this applies to any religious leader seen as all-embracing by his followers. We do not have to be bigots to be faithful. In fact Jesus reserves his scorn for those who consider themselves to be completely orthodox, and faithful, and justified. And you can be a bigot for any cause, be it Roman, Anglican, Nonconformist, Muslim, Hindu, atheist, humanist, Marxist, etc.

Is not the true Christ larger than our small minds can imagine, even when reading the Bible? Can we believe in a God who would exclude from his love those who, through no fault of their own, have given their commitment to the nearest and best ideal which they can understand? Is there anything in the gospel which could lead us to suppose that Jesus would turn his back on a practising Muslim just because he is a practising Muslim?

If Christianity is to be a universal religion, a religion with universal appeal, then it must appeal to people of all cultures and have room for people who honestly present themselves. This does not mean that we cease to believe and bear witness in our own way, but that we do not try to limit the scope of divine grace and the universal salvific will of God. A religion has to take root in some culture. It is not reasonable to expect everyone to belong to European culture, or to belong to the culture of the Holy Land in the time of Jesus. No one can live by the Bible alone. Indeed, no one is meant to live by the Bible alone. How can any book filled with the limitations of human language be the whole of life for anyone?

The Bible is a vehicle of revelation and needs to be lived, not just read. And it needs to be lived in a community which has its own nature, upon which grace can build. We are not abstract beings, but need to celebrate and take part in the life of our planet, our country, our neighbourhood, our worshipping community. We need resources for the body, for the mind, for the Spirit, in prayer and symbol and activity. How else can we be fully alive?

Weakness Versus Power

In one of our meetings we were reminded of a theology of weakness, an authenticity that does not rely on human power and respectability. St Paul is surely the patron of this. And here comes the rub. Is there not, under the guise of fundamentalism of any kind, an ever-present danger that we have a more human agenda? We may feel safe if the message is simplistic and contains no mystery. We may feel threatened if the way we have grown up and its securities are being threatened. We may want to be revenged on people who have persecuted us and our like in the past, and may threaten to do so again. We may want to have control of minds and hearts.

Would Hezbollah be such a violent sect if it had not suffered as part of a Shiite minority for a long time both religiously and politically? What may be a comfortable doctrine inside a ghetto may be a very dangerous one outside. And there are many respectable ghettos. They occur wherever a body of like-minded people are gathered, either because they have an exclusive privilege or they have been herded together as undesirable and infectious. And you can come out from persecution and find that you are now captured by the mentality of it, so that you in turn become a persecutor.

Surely the danger today is to be found in the direction of lack of relationship, rather than in any failure to be dogmatic. Is it that we feel better when everyone around feels and thinks the same way as we do? The more exclusive you become, the more you drive others to band together in the same way for the cause from which you have excluded them, and the less you can come into the open to share in any depth. We can become polite but we cannot grow together. I would find a more convincing divine presence in a group of welcoming non-Christians than in a group of narrow-minded Christians. There is the paradox of the universalist being angry with a cover-up, and becoming the scapegoat for being angry, thus relieving the others of any responsibility.

Sincerity and Openness

A working party concerned with dying and death, ultimate issues, surely has a need for special sincerity and openness. We cannot short-change patients and carers alike with anything less than the truth as we are able to show it, with humility and no pretence, even if this means a report which is more like a cry from the heart than a rationalist formula. Being an old hand with working parties I know how the need to produce a respectable document can take precedence over everything else. Yet it is better not to disguise differences once we are sure that they are not just misunderstandings. If we want to be effective we must take the necessary risk of not finishing with a glossy surface.

In the last few years we have seen how the Leninist face of Eastern Europe, which seemed to be so solidly in place, has melted away to reveal the same religious and national differences which were around in 1914. Can we not afford to show our feelings a little more? A difficult job for the chairman but, if we really get to know one another and have genuine respect, it will be a recognizable witness and a pioneering experience. The prospect of death should concentrate attention in a way which does not seem open to religious institutions when they discuss their differences. So while we need humour, sometimes desperately, we also need to take ourselves very seriously when we think of the work which has been entrusted to us.

15   LIVING WITH CONFLICT

"A really alive person is not merely someone who has a taste for life, but somebody who spreads that taste, showering it, as it were, around him; and a person who is really alive in this way has, quite apart from any tangible achievements of his, something essentially creative about him."[1]

Our first vocation is to be human. For this we are born. Our faith, whether Christian, Muslim, Sikh, Buddhist, Hindu, Jewish, Bahai, Humanist or Marxist, shapes our view of what it means to be human. Thus diversity and difference provide a wide spectrum of values as we search for the fullest meaning of our humanity.

We are members one of another and children of our culture. The way we regard 'being human' stems from an accident of birth which often dictates our culture and religion. In Britain at the end of the twentieth century individualism is in the ascendant, and minority cultures both here and throughout the world are trying to retain identity by isolation and struggle for independence. A human tendency towards divisiveness persists. We have not learned the secret of our humanity, namely that we cannot be independent of the love at the heart of the universe nor unrelated to our fellow creatures and the life of the planet. The heart of the Christian vision of humanness is relatedness. In the beginning God breathed his own breath of life into the creature which he had formed from the earth (Gen.1.27). This in-breathed spirit gives every human being life and relatedness in the image of

221

God. Within our understanding of the Godhead, relationship is enshrined in the Trinity. God has revealed the divine nature as threefold, a communion of love. Therefore we are human when we love God and our neighbour as ourselves (Mark 12.28-34). "This is a law of our nature not simply for our nature",[2] i.e. this is how God has made us to be.

There is today a growing understanding of our relationship to the planet. The 'dominion' of the earth entrusted to humanity (Gen.1.28) is often misinterpreted in terms of domination and exploitation. Jesus's teaching leaves us in no doubt that domination must give place to service and stewardship (Mark 10.42-45; John 13.3-17). And in the New Testament Jesus is seen as the origin of all creation (John 1.1-3; Col.1.15-20). The Green and Ecology Movements are unfolding what such responsibility might mean for humanity. The inter-connectedness of all things and the self-regulation of the planet's environment has led to the hypothesis that the planet is a single living organism.[3] We live in the earth, not merely on it.

How we fulfil our vocation to be human is moulded by our understanding of the nature of God - we grow like the things to which we give our attention. God reveals the divine nature through:

- the Bible
- the worship and tradition of the Church
- the words of prophets
- history
- the creation
- contemporary experience in personal relationships, political events, and community life.

In Christian thought, God is known pre-eminently in Jesus Christ. So St John is able to write that it is Jesus who brings fullness of life for humanity (John 10.10). It is in and through

222

the word of God made flesh that Christians both see what fullness of humanity is and find resources for humanization. The Bible helps us to live fully. The Bible was made for man, not man for the Bible (cp. Mark 2.27).

Two groups of people with varied experience in life and work - some of whom work in hospices and others with experience of the Church's ministry of healing - met in this Working Party and shared their beliefs and experience. Corporately, they acknowledged the importance of relatedness in the search for truth in all its facets. The members of the Working Party believe that they learned something about being human in today's world, from three points of view:

● the hospice
● the healing ministry
● a group of Christians who have learned to find difference an enrichment rather than a threat.

The Testimony of Hospice Staff

Hospice staff who constantly work in the face of human dying have shared their experience of human suffering and tragedy. Desperate situations of psychosocial anguish are met and shared on the basis of our common humanity. This anguish is sharpened for staff by compassion which involves a **reduction** in professional defences, such as distancing oneself from people in distress. The price of human solidarity is high. Society generally rejects all mention of death as morbid, preferring denial to acceptance of this reality of life.

Hospice staff not only have to bear their own feelings but also the projected fears and anger of others - patients, patients' relatives and colleagues. The injection of negative feelings into staff results in stress, and sometimes illness or breakdown, unless these feelings can be safely discharged or transformed. It is all too easy to take such feelings home and express them to the detriment of spouse, children or friends. Shakespeare and the Greek playwrights, for example, well understood the wider social effects of negative feelings and provided a means of corporate catharsis through drama.

Sometimes, however, there is value in receiving the negative feelings of others, anguish, criticism or rejection, into ourselves and bearing them:

> "We have to allow ourselves to be open to pain... If we are able to do this, to act, as it were, as blotting paper... without handing it on in the form of bitterness and resentment or of hurt to others - then somehow in some incomprehensible miracle of grace, some at least of the darkness may be turned to light." [4]

This solidarity with Christ's reconciling work involves bearing the suffering and so transforming it in the order of divine love and relationship. Such a process of 'absorbing darkness' is a necessary and potentially creative task in building community. It may be necessary to feel free to be angry with God. A hospice doctor writes:

> "I turn to the Bible, to David's psalms, and discover a principle that when emotionally shell-shocked by the battles of life, I should vent my frustration and anger on God... For David, described as a man after God's own heart, and for me, there was and is no other way... **Damn it, God, I cannot cope!** There is so much suffering, so much apparent unfairness... Being angry with God is a necessity for me. Without this avenue of release, I could not continue as a hospice physician." [5]

But our minds are conditioned by the culture in which we live. The task of cultural change is therefore part of the task of becoming more human. The burden of human anguish which surrounds death could be more equitably shared by a change of social attitudes to suffering, death, bereavement and widowhood. For the sake of our common humanity, this needs to be worked out in:

- parental upbringing of children
- education
- theological thought and pastoral practice.

We need to learn to live with an awareness of our mortality. To be human is to be vulnerable, and we have this treasure in an 'earthenware jar' (2 Cor.4.7). Frail people are capable of great acts of love.

Cultural change is slow and painful work. In this context, the Christian understanding of the long-term transformation of the world through suffering love finds an earthed expression in the hospice. The hospice is a place of strength through weakness where:

- acceptance of suffering
- bearing one's cross for the benefit of others
- prayers of self-offering to God in a situation of powerlessness

help in God's work of transforming darkness into light. On the Cross, Jesus not only cried out "My God, My God, why have you forsaken me?" (Matt.27.46) but also "It is accomplished!" (John 19.30).

The testimony of hospice staff calls our attention to the awful reality of Good Friday. If the glory of Easter resurrection is allowed to prettify the tragedy and shock of Good Friday then the depth of the Incarnation - God's solidarity with all people in their suffering and mortality - is not plumbed. Jesus descended into hell before he ascended into heaven. It was through a terrible death that the whole creation has been saved (Col.1.15-23; Rom.8.19-23). This costliness is built into God's chosen method of creation, namely, **transformation of evil through suffering love** (see chapter 6).

The bulwark against isolation and alienation is solidarity, but the cost is high. Hospice staff bear witness to the need for membership, not only of a team but also of a community of support such as family, friends or church congregation. Contemporary concern with 'community' bears witness to a hunger to belong which is not easily satisfied in our present society. But hospice staff have learned that solidarity with fellow human beings is a necessary component of health. Grief and anger need to be shared if they are not merely to be burdens to be borne (sometimes to the point of breaking) but also transformed into a springboard for personal growth and deeper relationships.

The Testimony of the Healing Ministry

One of the factors in the re-birth of the Church's ministry of healing was a rebellion against the Victorian resignation which made it possible for parents to put 'Thy will be done' on the gravestone of a child who had died of diphtheria. The Church's ministry of healing was a radical protest against such a concept of God. Those who work for the healing of the sick, whether through prayer, anointing, medicine or surgery, are therefore sensitive to any 'throwing in of the towel' before the utmost efforts have been expended in trying to change anything which mars, stunts or imprisons a human person. This attitude, based on one interpretation of the healing ministry of Jesus, contains some denial of illness and death. It is nonetheless based on a healthy response to the ravages of evil, seeking to transform it into even greater possibilities of human stature.

In 1970 the Churches' Council of Healing changed its name to the Churches' Council for Health and Healing. This was a significant change, in recognition that 'prevention is better than cure' and that promotion of health is the creative purpose which subsumes both the cure and the prevention of disease. This insight grew from the recognition of *shalom* as an Old Testament image of health, and 'the Kingdom of God' as a New Testament parallel, - both images of personal and social harmony, i.e. right-relatedness (see chapter 7). The understanding of 'salvation' as right-relatedness leads straight into the work of building healthy community life, whether in home, school, hospital ward, or shop floor. It also leads straight into the service of healing illness in a society where today such a high proportion of illness and disharmony appears to be caused by broken personal relationships, poverty, bad housing, and child-neglect.[6] If we really want people to be healthier, we must concentrate on issues such as:

- the environment
- housing
- lifestyle
- the nature and conditions of work
- the quality of agriculture and food production.

Our present compartmentalization of religion often prevents us from recognizing such political matters as concerns of the Kingdom of God for healthy human life.

Compassion is at the heart of the Church's ministry of healing. Solidarity in human suffering is the spur to action:

> "And those who follow compassion
> find life for themselves,
> justice for their neighbour,
> and glory for God." [7]

Solidarity in suffering is a necessary complement to the work of healers because a 'Yes' to life keeps us human, whether we are dealing with victory over or defeat by disease and disability. The work of the healer, whether in prevention, cure or just bearing the burden of illness, needs to be done with great compassion but also great detachment: "Teach us to care and not to care".[8] It is important not to be discouraged because no 'results' are visible. There is great power in not being held hostage to results. There is need for faith as a working relationship with a God who involves us in his play [9,10] and who cannot be judged by our digital calculators. Compassion takes us from the scintillating television-worthy specialities, such as heart transplants, to the bedside care of a dying pauper whose immeasurable worth stems from the fact that God loves and suffers with him. Compassion means suffering with someone, giving someone 'creative attention'. There are many people whom we can help little except by being there.

The Testimony of the Working Party

1. Living with conflict

The Working Party began work together with all the familiar academic arguments about health, healing, wholeness and salvation. Those with the most vital spiritual experience stemming from bedside work with dying people were largely silenced by such erudition. Thus, the first conflict derived from **problems with language**. Slowly, however, much of the baggage members had brought with them was off-loaded. This included the hard work of detachment from cherished ideas. It was quickly appreciated how words may have different content for people of different temperament, maturity and experience. Perhaps the Working Party was fortunate in that it did not contain anyone from faiths other than Christian, or cultures other than Western. Otherwise the differences could have been overwhelming. An inter-faith Working Party, however, would be a natural follow-up to this one.

Members discovered and learned to respect a plurality of Christian beliefs and attitudes among themselves. This plurality of beliefs and attitudes also arose from differences of personality, experience, and from nurture in different Christian denominations; and from the partiality of each member's glimpses of God's truth in Jesus. It was also partly because of the paradoxical nature of truth, as evidenced again and again in the Gospel narratives, and epitomized by the dictum of Niels Bohr, the physicist:

"The opposite of a correct statement is a false statement. But the opposite of a profound truth may well be another profound truth."

To be human includes being caught up in the conflict of opposites. Finding a balance is the work of a lifetime. Meanwhile, according to training and temperament, people take up positions, sometimes more extreme for the sake of principle, sometimes inclined to compromise for the sake of peace. When concerned with issues of life and death the conflict tends to be thrown into higher relief. Identifying issues and finding the way through results in personal growth, however painful it may be. As long as there is trust and respect among the individuals involved, a group will become enriched and enlivened. It will not be in danger of fleeing from reality to take refuge in a comfortable illusion.

It was accepted that theology must be rooted in everyday experience - which meant beginning at the bedside. But old habits die hard. However, as the Working Party prayed together, wrestled together and ate together, its common humanity began to prevail. In the vastness of its ignorance the members were all struggling for a glimpse of truth greater than each other's partial points of view. It is doubtful if a written report can convey how the Working Party experienced this. Truth-discovered is golden, truth-told is silver. And there are no short cuts to its discovery. Therefore such light as was glimpsed about humanness is presented as testimony, rather than as a chain of logical arguments.

Slowly the members of the Working Party learned to live with conflict as a fact of Christian community. At the level of theory, ideas, theology and beliefs there was some agreement and some persistent disagreement. But because of a common commitment to Jesus, members became reconciled to one another as human beings. The words of Jesus provided the key: "I am the truth" (John 14.6). Truth is not simply a series of statements. God sent a son, Jesus of Nazareth, born when Quirinius governed Syria. He is our source of unity despite our conflicts. He is the source of that fullness of humanity towards which people reach out.

It was a clash of pastoral practices at the bedside which had originally led to the setting up of the Working Party (see Case History 5, p 58). In that instance the pastoral care of a dying person in a hospice was challenged by a style of pastoral care which promised healing by faith of a fatal illness. The consequent confusion caused added spiritual suffering for the patient and her family.

A further cause of conflict was exposed by a survey carried out in a number of hospices to find out the beliefs of staff about 'after death' and heaven and hell.[11] It was discovered that the majority of hospice staff become 'universalists', that is, they come to believe that most, and possibly all, people will be saved. For example, if a nurse believes:
- everyone is of worth in God's eyes
- Christ cares through her hands for those who suffer

- she embodies the love of God for that person, indeed that Christ himself may be represented in that person (Matt.25.40)

how can she a moment later, when the patient has died, believe in a God who throws that person into the flames of hell? Bedside spirituality is in conflict with one interpretation of scripture (Matt.25.41; Mark 9.42-48; Luke 10.13-15). There are texts in the Bible which seem to emphasize the selectiveness of divine choice:

"There is no salvation through anyone else [than Christ]." (Acts 4.12)

But there are others which emphasize the universality of human destiny:

"As in Adam all die, so in Christ all will be brought to life." (1 Cor.15.22)

Europe was ravaged with religious wars over many centuries because of controversies about:

- what is needed for salvation
- who are the ones God has selected
- how the selection is made
- what is the authentic body to which one must belong in order to be saved.

Obedience to the letter of 'proof texts', however, is a sure way to kill the spirit of the Bible.

These conflicts appear to be based on theological differences but more probably relate to differences of personality, particularly in regard to use of authority. The way people perceive the authority of the Bible is in great measure the result of the pattern of parenting received as children.[12] The authority figures of childhood shape the way authority is given to God, and the way authority figures like the police are responded to in daily life. People tend to grow out of childish patterns of behaviour, however, unless tragically they suffer arrested growth.

A conflict in approaches to bedside pastoral care was raised by evangelism. If it is believed that someone must overtly turn to Christ before death in order to be saved, then hospice staff who hold such a belief will be under pressure to obtain a death-bed repentance. The professional ethic of nurses and doctors, however, would regard such an approach to a patient as an abuse of their professional position. The underlying question here is the very nature of evangelism: is it one person telling another what's what, or is it a shared exploration involving further change in the evangelist? But, in any case, who has the right to force the door of a sufferer's wounded *sanctum*?

The Working Party kept a list of 'nettles to be grasped' to try to prevent differences being swept under the carpet. This relentlessly led, through a common search, into deeper questions about the nature of God. Who is God for us today? It was from the different answers to this question that all previous conflicts flowed. Questions about God arose at once from the human suffering experienced by members of the Working Party in their daily hospice or other pastoral work. Does God also suffer? Can God enter into human suffering? In traditional theology God has been described as 'impassible', that is, not susceptible to suffering (see chapter 2). Although this may describe God's transcendent nature, hospice staff particularly found such a seemingly remote God entirely unhelpful in coping with everyday suffering.

Christians as "members of the body of Christ" (1 Cor.12.27) carry Christ's presence with them into every human situation.

The Incarnation invites us to see God as indwelling our human situations, knowing it from the inside. The Cross is God's word of empathy with human suffering.

For some people, God is the one who stands over and beyond us asking for unconditional acceptance of his authority and giving us an unalterable law. This would include obedience to an institution speaking with his authority. God and his ministers stand above us offering forgiveness and salvation. But the Holy Spirit is not restricted to working with institutions which are often bureaucratic, insensitive and power-seeking. Other people stress the presence of God within each one of us. God breathed his spirit into the clay of humanity at the creation (Gen.2.7). The whole world is sacred. We are co-creators with God in ordering and evolving it in a sacred manner.

There are conflicts between outward loyalty and inward vision. A hospice community at worship may feel the tension between denominational loyalty and its own truths experienced day by day in clinical and nursing care. It is through this everyday experience of suffering that we have glimpsed the dark side of God, and cannot in all honesty tame the terror of that experience. God is seen to be very destructive in the working out of his purpose.

"I was struck recently by a remark from someone who told me she had left the Church because it was all too **happy**... She was objecting to what she saw as the Church's determination to conceal all traces of evil and conflict. Terrified that its story and dogmas might not fit the world's experience of reality, the Church conspired, she claimed, to alter that reality. So from Sunday school songs to funeral sermons to episcopal moral directives an impression was given that all was really good in the creation of the good God and that a benign Saviour would remove any trace of ill. True, sin and suffering entered the story, but only as counters to be pushed aside by the masterstroke of resurrection."[13]

One of the tasks of hospice staff within the Working Party has been to bring the anger and rebellion of Job into the ordered (and sometimes idealized) world of the healers, thereby moving members towards a new awareness of God, comprehensive enough to contain both the terror and glory of creation. The creation is a book about God. We need a new honesty to God. The tragedies met in hospices can rarely be ascribed to people's own fault. The apparent unfairness of life is starkly exposed. We can sympathize with the *cri de coeur* 'How can God let all this happen?' Or perhaps more poignantly 'How did God come to make us like this?' The question is not so much about arbitrary suffering as about the mystery of God. Perhaps we try too often to tidy and tame God rather than face a more awesome reality. Before the mystery of God, words fail: "The teaching about Christ begins with silence."

These are some of the nettles which the Working Party tried to grasp, as it learned to live with conflict. But this means more than putting up with conflict like a toothache. Certainly when we disagree we have a pain problem. However, to live with conflict means to change, particularly to:

- discover what newness of life as a Christian means
- recognize that theological statements are tied to time and culture
- let God shatter our images of the divine nature again and again.

This means transcending conflict in a suffering love where our knowledge **about** God, neighbour and self is accepted as partial (without denying that partial knowledge is true knowledge), and our knowledge **of** God, neighbour and self is a mystery we respect. This is not to deny the importance of our God-given intellect, but to put intellectual work into the wider context of right-relatedness, and discover how the life of love and the life of the intellect may be bound together (Phil.1.9-10).

But why conflict? When someone expresses an idea with which one disagrees, why not an expression of interest in a strange viewpoint? Or just a shrug of the shoulders? Why the need to argue, to attack?

People strive to reach synthesis, consensus and deeper understanding through dialogue and debate. Differences and disagreements are uncomfortable realities which have to be accepted in a situation where knowledge is partial. They can also be pegs on which to hang an inner agenda. None who has watched a lecturer demolish the arguments of an adversary can fail to sense the powerful emotions involved, and the almost Tarzan-like triumph of the final thrust. Academic argument can be a socially acceptable way in which to discharge aggression.

People attack in others the faults which they suppress in themselves. They attack in others the habits and views which are rooted in the unconscious mind. Thus the person who is very punitive towards liars is the person who fears an inner propensity for being economical with the truth. The fundamentalist and the anti-fundamentalist both have an equal tendency towards authoritarianism. Conflict can be a gruelling road to self-knowledge. This is as true for nations as for individuals. Although there is reality in the United Nations going to war to stop an aggressive dictator, there is also a dark and inner agenda in the spirit of the nations (particularly Western) who attack in the enemy their own power-seeking and authoritarian desire to shape the other after their own image. We human beings are mirrors to one another. And what appears in the reflection has to be brought to consciousness and lived; for it is a despised and feared part of ourselves which will come back time and time again demanding to be lived.

Therefore conflict has a voice. We learn most from the people who threaten us most, and from the things which we abhor and reject. It was the stone which the builders rejected which became the cornerstone of the new building (Mark 12.10). This was Christ's message in regard to the outcasts and rejected - they had most to teach their oppressors.

Living with conflict is not a simple matter of bearing disagreements. A necessary first step is to accept the whole of life in its ambiguity, frustration, suffering and limitations. Then we must move on to learn **through** conflict what it is in ourselves which we are rejecting, and how to accept and digest it. In making strength through weakness (2 Cor.12.8), God gives us a road to renewal. Liberation is achieved through the given circumstances. That is a description of what is involved in *metanoia* (repentance):

- a very painful change of attitude or value
- a grief process to be worked through
- a death to be died as the way through to resurrection and renewal.

The writer of 'A Cry from the Heart' (chapter 14) was therefore correct to speak about the need for the expression of anger in the Working Party. There is not only the anger near the surface which we are quick to use in defence or attack:

> "He who is angry or afraid is not praised or blamed, but only he who, while in this state, behaves either properly or not. Though anger coming after a rational judgement upsets the reason, nevertheless it is useful because it

gives greater promptitude in carrying out the commands of the reason. Coming before a judgement, however, anger is bad, as it makes a true judgement almost impossible."[14]

It is important to know how to use anger constructively. Jesus used anger to break through a circle of prejudice ranged against him (Mark 3.1-6). The cleansing of the temple may be a good example of controlled anger (John 2.14). But there is also a deeper anger which is part of the anguish of learning through experience. The grief process of repentance involves anger as much as the grief process of any loss. It is part of the pain of the human learning process. We could therefore say further that living with conflict is:

- a disclosure of self-knowledge
- a learning opportunity
- to repent until "seventy times seven" (Matt.18.22)
- necessary 'growing pains'.

The Working Party did not always reach a sufficient depth of trust to permit overt anger. Perhaps we are still too near to our parents' generation for whom anger was sinful?

2. Compassion

It has already been noted that compassion is part of the motivation for those who work in hospices. This stems partly from a sense of human solidarity but also from the realization that suffering love is God's chosen method of creation. God is love, and love means suffering love. People are co-creators with God in the daily re-making of themselves, their patients, their colleagues and their common life, as they build right-relatedness with one another. In the Christian view becoming fully human is both a suffering and a joy. It would be possible to become morbid about this, but:

Man was made for Joy and Woe,
And once this we rightly know
Through the world we safely go.
Joy and Woe are woven fine
A clothing for the soul divine.
Under every grief and pine
Runs a joy with silken twine.[15]

St Paul writes: "In our sorrows we have always cause for joy" (2 Cor.6.10). Fullness of humanity in this age contains the sorrow of not being whole. A whole human being will be complete only in the age to come. In our present age, however, a mature person is an amalgam of greatness and brokenness. The creation is one. Pain and joy, death and loss come ultimately from the single reality of God. To love God, and our neighbour as our incomplete self, requires suffering love. We are to rekindle a reverence for humanness encompassing both light and shadow.

3. Healing and dying

The Working Party concluded that both the care of the dying and the ministry of healing are one whole ministry together. They complement one another. They have often been separated in practice when the words 'healing' and 'curing' have been misunderstood as synonymous.

Certainly we must resist every crippling disease which threatens to diminish our humanity, right up to the point where we realize that victory is not being given.[16] At that point activity gives place to acceptance. But that still does not involve a hopeless resignation. Acceptance that I am dying can still mean that every day of remaining life can be lived to the full in terms of whatever activities are possible, and in rich relationship with others.

The 'ministry of healing' does not give way to 'care of the dying' at the point where resistance gives place to acceptance. Patients in a hospice, who receive the laying on of hands, for example, may experience the gift of "peace that passes all understanding" (Phil.4.7). Indeed there is a sense in which the ministry of healing includes the care of the dying just because its inmost meaning is a consummation in right-relatedness with God, neighbour and self: and the fact that one is dying does not preclude such a grace. A hospice may therefore more realistically be called a 'home of healing' than a place which promotes unrealistic expectations of cure of disease.

Those in the Working Party within the ministry of healing recognized that some forms of the ministry of healing to the sick made claims and raised expectations which properly belong to the age to come. The Kingdom of God is not only 'now' but also 'not yet'. The perfect reign of God is of its nature something which belongs to the End. It is God's will that death shall be done away and sorrow and pain shall be no more (Rev.21.4), but it is evidently not God's will that death shall be done away with in this present age. This is part of our given humanity.

It requires great maturity of judgement to know when the point has been reached when one must cease to fight an illness and accept it passively, living within the increasingly narrow constraints of the situation.[17] The ministry of healing and curing becomes the ministry of healing and caring, but together they comprise an integrated agency for the mediation of God's love to suffering humanity.

"Grant us, O Lord, the courage to change the things which can be changed, the strength to bear the things which cannot be changed, and the wisdom to know the difference."

239

References

1   Marcel G. *The Mystery of Being.* (Gifford Lectures, Vol 1). Harvill Press, London 1949, p 139.
2   Auden WH. Sermon in Westminster Abbey to an invited congregation of scientists. 1966.
3   Lovelock JE. *Gaia.* Oxford University Press, Oxford 1979.
4   Spufford M. *Celebration.* Collins-Fount, London 1986, p 92.
5   Twycross RG. *A Time to Die.* CMF Publications, London 1984, p 14.
6   Bird A. *The Search for Health: A Response from the Inner City.* Institute for the Study of Worship and Religious Architecture, University of Birmingham, Birmingham 1981.
7   Fox M. *Meditations with Meister Eckhart.* Bear, Santa Fe 1983, p 102.
8   Eliot TS. 'Ash Wednesday I'. In: *The Complete Poems and Plays of TS Eliot.* Faber & Faber, London 1969.
9   Huizinga J. *Homo Ludens: A Study of the Play-Element in Culture.* Trans RFC Hull. Routledge & Kegan Paul, London 1949.
10 Kinsley D. *The Divine Player: A Study of the Kṛṣṇa. Eīlā.* Motilal Banarsidass, Delhi 1979.
11 Woodroffe I. *Towards a Hospice Theology.* St George's House, Windsor 1989.
12 Nurses Christian Movement. *Christianity and Nursing Today.* Epworth, London 1964.
13 Burdon C. *Stumbling on God.* SPCK, London 1990, p 5.
14 Aquinas T. *The Human Wisdom of St Thomas.* Pieper J (ed). Sheed & Ward, London 1948, p 286-287.
15 Blake W. '*Auguries of Innocence*'. In: Keynes G (ed). *Complete Writings.* Oxford University Press, Oxford 1966, p 432.
16 Teilhard de Chardin. *Le Milieu Divin.* (English Translation). Collins, London 1960.
17 Vanstone WH. *The Stature of Waiting.* Darton, Longman & Todd, London 1982.

INDEX